## What's Being Said

"My relationship with my wife improved as a result of this class. She saw me interact and react to issues that were discussed in class and in the homework. It showed her that I do care about our relationship and the children. Participating in this class helped me to realize that my attitude towards my stepchildren can really influence their lives. This makes me think twice before I comment or react to situations that arise."

—Pete

"This has been the best class we've ever taken. First, and most importantly, I have a more complete relationship with God. Second, I now step back and look at the overall aspect of every issue. I listen more now to my husband and don't expect him to react in the same way I do. The week on finances helped my husband to see things he has not been able to see until now. Being in a group of other couples, sharing the same problems, really helped me feel pretty normal."

—Sue

"We have learned how to communicate as a family. I have learned to set aside my anger and jealousy and welcome the Lord into my life. I now understand that without God's word we have no foundation to build our life upon. This class has given me wisdom, strength, and tools to succeed. I absolutely feel this class is a must for bringing families of second marriages together."

—Heather

"Participating in this class has helped me to focus on issues that have not opened up yet, but will in the future, and to be prepared for them. By practicing the suggestions given for family meetings we can focus on improving relationships with our stepchildren. The chapters spent talking about children's issues and ex spouses in blending both families were important weeks for me."

—Brian

"I never realized the part that guilt and shame played in our earlier years of marriage until I read this chapter! This is a great class. I learned a lot, and it helped me to realize the commitment to my new family is worth it."

—Debbie

"This class brought home how improving my relationship with Jesus is the key to being able to persevere in the challenges ahead. I like how this class covers many problems pertaining to relationships, like anger, attitude, and money."

—John P.

"This class helped me to recall and reexamine earlier times in our own blended family experience. My greatest improvement has been working on ways to make each person feel special; to try to help give positive attitudes."

—John I.

"Understanding that conflict is a natural part of the blending process helped me. I can now see the hurdles in my life as well as the positives, and I am thankful for the problems we don't have going on that others shared about."

—Kerry

"We realized the need to share responsibilities as a parenting team in raising our three boys. At the same time, we were greatly encouraged to balance this responsibility with the nurturing of our own adult relationship. I can see results already."

—Garth

# BLENDED FAMILIES

# *Workbook*

# BLENDED FAMILIES

# *Workbook*

A Study Guide to *Blended Families*

## CREATING HARMONY AS YOU BUILD A NEW HOME LIFE

MAXINE MARSOLINI

Printed in the United States of America

Packaged by Pleasant Word, a division of WinePress Publishing, PO Box 428, Enumclaw, WA 98022. The views expressed or implied in this work do not necessarily reflect those of Pleasant Word, a division of WinePress Publishing. Ultimate design, content, and editorial accuracy of this work are the responsibilities of the author.



ISBN 1-4141-0181-3
Library of Congress Catalog Card Number: 2004092533

# Dedication

The *Blended Families Workbook* is dedicated to Tom and Elizabeth Dressel for their seemingly tireless devotion to strengthening the family. You are both great encouragers as you truly believe that every marriage matters. Because you prayed for resources for the blended family, we came to know one another. Because you asked, this workbook was written.

# *Table of Contents*

# Acknowledgments

I want to thank a handful of special people who were instrumental in the completion of the *Blended Families Workbook*. Their encouragement was priceless. At the top of the list is my grammatically correct friend, Linda Porter Carlyle. Linda gave hours upon hours of editing and practical insights with such a happy heart—and many an iced mocha.

The pursuing interest of Laurence and Wendy Dunn resulted in the very first small group study with the *Blended Families Workbook*. The Dunns, not part of a blended family themselves, were looking for ways to offer help to the large number of blended families within their church body. Thank you, Laurence and Wendy, for giving of yourselves so generously. After the first night, we were certain God had drawn this group together. Men and women affirmed their pent-up need to talk about what it's really like to be part of a blended family. The workbook materials moved us with ease from one talking point to another. The enthusiasm, honesty, and willingness to learn put these materials to the test. How exciting it was when couples came back the next week feeling victorious at having put a new idea into practice!

Last, I want to thank my husband, Charlie, for his support. You and I know our blended journey has not been without bump or bruise. Only we can appreciate how, with the Lord's help, our family has grown. We both agree that seeing Jesus as our hope is the reason we've been able to hang in there when the going got tough. I am so grateful that you listened to the Lord and as a team we embraced His answers for our family. Thank you for believing I had a workbook in me that needed to get into print.

# Introduction to The Blended Families Workbook

The *Blended Families Workbook* is broken into two complete six-week units. This gives the freedom to use the workbook as two six-week units, independent of one another, or as a continuous twelve-week study. On some occasions, a group may want to further adapt the workbook to three four-week units. That is also accomplished very easily. The *Blended Families Workbook* is a study guide to *Blended Families, Creating Harmony as You Build a New Home Life* (ISBN# 0-8024-3056-2).

BLENDED FAMILIES are nontraditional families created by divorce (whether you remarry or not), death of a mate, adoption, foster parenting, or a close relative taking on the parenting responsibilities in the absence of the biological parents. These people do not all share the same biological histories. Instead, they share a common thread. Every blended family is built upon the loss of the former family unit.

In the beginning, each newly formed family believes it will succeed. Many are convinced that God has given them a second chance at family life. The problem is these households are fragile by nature. Most of these people will find they need help to cope with the demands of changed lives and to keep discouragement from taking up residence in their hearts. The *Blended Families Workbook* offers that kind of help.

## Purpose

1. To recognize good blending doesn't mean life will be smooth all the time. Even ice cream has chunks of chocolate and fruit mixed in.

2. To set realistic family goals
3. To nurture a healthy marriage
4. To examine the role the past has played
5. To understand the teamwork of co-parenting
6. To build up and encourage the children to succeed
7. To move from crisis thinking to outcome thinking
8. To consider the effects of birth order and personality on the family
9. To develop an agreed-upon plan for financial unity
10. To express anger in ways that lead to healthy solutions
11. To bring resolve to behaviors that undermine the family
12. To be aware of the reasons why we show respect to an ex and cultivate inter-family relationships
13. To challenge each participant to make the most of his or her blended journey
14. To feel the hope God has promised our families

The initial emotional climate of the blended family can be best defined as two opposite sets of emotions caught in a tug-of-war to find balance:

A. A bright new beginning is perceived = hope
B. A private mourning for the loss of prior relationships = grief

As you begin this study, take a moment to reflect. Ask the hard questions. If your answer to any of these questions is less than ideal, then this workbook is for you.

1. How well am I coping with my blended family? Am I living in denial of the grief, focusing the lion's share of my attention on the new life while stuffing the sad feelings that remain from my past family?
2. Do I act out my dissatisfaction with life in aggressive, or suppressive, ways with both the new and the old family systems?
3. Is harmony or disharmony found in greater measure at my house?
4. Is my heart open to change?

## Who can benefit from the *Blended Families Workbook*?

1. This workbook is available to any individual who is interested in knowing more about the blended family: Those already remarried, those contemplating remarriage, people who are thinking of divorce, as well as counselors, pastors, teachers, and lay people who want to increase their understanding of the blended family.
2. The workbook's *optimum* potential comes when it is chosen as a study for small groups made up of six to eight couples. The bonding and sharing of ideas, struggles, and joys is nurturing to everyone. Blendeds learn they are not alone in their feelings. They now have a safe place to talk about what's going on in their emotions and with their

stepfamily. A group made up of both singles and couples should represent no more than eight family units so everyone has an opportunity to share. Make sure you are counting your leaders as well.

3. The *Blended Families Workbook* can also be used to facilitate a larger one-day seminar to the blended family or a series of six or twelve consecutive meetings.

## What you'll need to know

1. Each week's lesson will take approximately two hours, just 20 minutes a day, outside of class. Look at this time as an investment in your family rather than a burden.
2. The *Blended Families Workbook* is a study guide to be used alongside the book, *Blended Families* ISBN# 0-8024-3056-2. You will need a copy of the book, *Blended Families,* by Maxine Marsolini.
3. The weekly lessons are easy to follow. At the end of each chapter you will find a Practical Application assignment for next week's class. The instructions will lead you to the *Workbook Enhancement Pages* located at the back of the workbook.
4. Come to class prepared, with your homework done, so you will be ready to contribute to the discussion and glean ideas from one another.
5. Be punctual. The group will need to start on time to finish on time.
6. Confidentiality is a must. This is the respectful way to nurture trust and bonding between class members.
7. Weekly meetings can be held where it is most convenient for the group: in homes, churches, or office facilities.
8. Classes meet once a week for no less than ninety minutes and if possible, two hours in length. It takes time to comfortably complete the sharing of the week's lesson in a relaxed manner.
9. A certificate of completion, found in the back of your workbook, is for those who have attended at least five lessons out of each six-week unit (a total of ten lessons). These certificates will be signed by your leader and witnessed by fellow class participants at the close of your last class. If you'd prefer to frame the certificates for your class, you may print them out with a colored logo by visiting the *www.blendedfamilies.net* web site for instructions on how to download the document.

## My group will meet

Date ______________ Day of the week ______________ Time __________

My leader is __________________________ Phone number _____________

Location of class ________________________________________

# *Mission Statement*

The purpose of the *Blended Families Workbook* is to equip merged families, whether created as a result of death, divorce, adoption, prior single parenting, or foster parenting, with life changing skills that are in agreement with the Word of God. It is believed that couples in blended families, who are determined to establish solid marriages and positive parenting skills, can impart healthy values just as effectively as a biological family.

## Author's Prayer

Lord, it is my prayer that those who use the *Blended Families Workbook* will find their families encouraged to live in ways that please You. I pray for a strong commitment from moms and dads for family survival. Where there are hurt feelings and grief has left its scars, help people to reach out to one another with forgiveness and comfort. Influence the parents so well that when their sons and daughters leave home, they will establish families that not only stand the test of time, but also ultimately strengthen the face of America.

May your families be richly blessed,<br>
Maxine Marsolini

# UNIT ONE

**To prepare for this study you will need a copy of the paperback book: *Blended Families, Creating Harmony as you Build a New Home Life*, Moody Press, 2000, by Maxine Marsolini. ISBN# 0-8024-3056-2**

## When You Thought I Wasn't Looking

When you thought I wasn't looking
You hung my first painting on the refrigerator
And I wanted to paint another.

When you thought I wasn't looking
You fed a stray cat
And I thought it was good to be kind to animals.

When you thought I wasn't looking
You baked a birthday cake just for me
And I knew that little things were special things.

When you thought I wasn't looking
You said a prayer
And I believed there was a God
That I could always talk to.

When you thought I wasn't looking
You kissed me goodnight
And I felt loved.

When you thought I wasn't looking
I saw tears come from your eyes
And I learned that sometimes things hurt—
But that it's alright to cry.

When you thought I wasn't looking
You smiled
And it made me want to look that pretty too.

When you thought I wasn't looking
You cared
And I wanted to be everything I could be.

When you thought I wasn't looking
I looked and wanted to say thanks
For all those things you did
When you thought I wasn't looking.[1]

by Mary Rita Schilke Korzan

# WEEK ONE

## *Expectations Run High*

*Finally, all of you, live in harmony with one another; be sympathetic, love as brothers, be compassionate and humble. Do not repay evil with evil or insult with insult, but with blessing, because to this you were called so that you may inherit a blessing.*

1 Peter 3:8–9

> Christopher Columbus' diary seems very repetitive at times. Page after page simply says, "This day we sailed on!" What a great motto for a blended family. Do you have a vision, a goal on the horizon, for your marriage? Is there a vision for your children or for your extended family? Goals are accomplished with perseverance—one day at a time.

**Read Chapter 1 of *Blended Families: And There Came a Lion***

**Take 15 minutes at the beginning of week one's class to introduce yourselves to one another.**

1. What insights did you find most helpful in Chapter 1?

_______________________________________________

_______________________________________________

2. It has been said that love is a dream and marriage is the alarm clock. We laugh, but why does this humorous statement seem even more applicable to the blended family?

Think back to your wedding day. What were your expectations and dreams for your new family? If you are not yet married, describe what you believe family life will look like after you say, "I do."

Which of these expectations have been realized?

Which of these expectations failed to materialize?

3. Be honest. How do you normally react when what you expect to happen turns into a major disappointment?

If you were to describe your spouse's reaction to the same disappointment, what would you say?

4. Read Jeremiah 29:11. How would you describe the hope found in this passage of Scripture?

   How do these promises from God make you feel?

5. July 4, 1952, was a foggy morning when Florence Chadwick waded into the water off Catalina Island. Her goal was to swim across the 21-mile channel from Catalina Island to the California coast. This wasn't an unachievable goal for Florence to set. She had been the first woman to swim the English Channel in both directions. That day the weather wasn't very cooperative. The water was numbingly cold, the fog was so thick she could barely see the boats in her party, and more than once sharks had to be driven away with rifle fire. Florence swam more than 15 hours before she asked to be taken out of the water. Her trainer tried to encourage her to keep going. He knew they were so close to land. But with every stroke of her arms Florence could only see the fog. So she quit. Later she discovered she'd quit only one mile from her goal.

"I'm not excusing myself, but if I could have seen the land I might have made it," she said. The cold, the fear of sharks, even the exhaustion didn't cause Florence Chadwick to fall short of her goal. What stopped her was the fog. She simply could not see where she was going.

We are sometimes a lot like Florence. We set out with a goal in sight but don't always make it to the finish line—not because we're afraid—but because we get discouraged and lose sight of our goal.

Two months later a brave Florence Chadwick decided to try again. She walked off the same beach into the same channel and swam the distance. Not only did she succeed at crossing the channel between Catalina Island and the California coast, she set a new speed record of 13 hours and 47 minutes. Why? The only thing that changed was the fact that this time Florence could see the land.

Have you ever felt a disappointment similar to Florence Chadwick's? What was your goal? What steps had you taken to put your goal in place?

________________________________________

________________________________________

________________________________________

________________________________________

Why do you think you failed?

________________________________________

________________________________________

________________________________________

________________________________________

6. Now, think of a time when you set a goal and your goal was realized. Why do you think this goal was realized? How did that victory make you feel?

________________________________________

________________________________________

________________________________________

________________________________________

7. Six reasons goals are important to the blended family:

   1. Goals help *define* our purpose.
   2. Goals set *boundaries* and *accountability* in place.
   3. Goals say "your dreams matter to me."
   4. Goals *map* the way to accomplishment.
   5. Goals push us toward *I can* thinking.
   6. Goals bring *abstract* time into *perspective*.

   Put into writing two goal statements for your family. The first goal should be something that can be reasonably accomplished within one to six months. The second goal should consider the BIG picture, and be a long-term goal, to be attained in anywhere from one to ten years.

   A. One short-term goal for our family is:

   ______________________________

   ______________________________

   ______________________________

   ______________________________

   We could attain this goal by _______ (date). Tell how this goal will be met.

   ______________________________

   ______________________________

   ______________________________

   ______________________________

   B. One long-term goal for our family is:

   ______________________________

   ______________________________

   ______________________________

   ______________________________

   We could attain this goal by _______ (date). Tell how this goal will be met.

   ______________________________

   ______________________________

I have shared these two goals with my spouse. ____ (yes/no)
He or she reacted with: (circle one)

1. Great enthusiasm.
2. Lack of interest.
3. Seen as foolish nonsense.

How did your partner's reaction make you feel?

8. 2 Timothy 4:16–18 tells a lot about Paul. What was happening to him at the time?

How had Paul's friends treated him?

What was the source of his deliverance?

Is there a circumstance in your life right now that would cause you to relate to Paul? Do you find encouragement from these verses?

________________________________________

________________________________________

________________________________________

________________________________________

**A Reflective Moment**

As we look back at our family's journey, we can see there've been lots of times when circumstances got the best of us. It's comforting to realize You already know the lions we've met and the ones that lie ahead. We can rely on Your faithfulness to protect us from discouragement. When days bring chaos, please draw our attention back to You, Lord, for a fresh reason to celebrate.

Guide us with Your unfailing wisdom to set wholesome goals in motion that will bless our family. We trust You will also provide the resources to see those goals realized.

**Practical Application for next week's lesson: Turn to page 125 of the Workbook Enhancement Pages. Read *Stay Close by for the Sake of the Kids.***

## WEEK TWO

# *The Reality of a New Family*

*Let your gentleness be evident to all. The Lord is near.*

Philippians 4:5

*Speak to one another with psalms, hymns, and spiritual songs. Sing and make music in your heart to the Lord, always giving thanks to God the Father for everything, in the name of our Lord Jesus Christ.*

Ephesians 5:19–20

**Nobility**

True worth is in being, not seeming,—
In doing, each day that goes by,
Some little good—
Not in dreaming of great things to do by and by.
For whatever men say in their blindness,
And spite of the fancies of youth,
There's nothing so kingly as kindness,
And nothing so royal as truth.

—Alice Cary (1820-1871)

**Read Chapter 2 of *Blended Families: From Naiveté to Reality***

1. What was your reaction after reading *Stay Close by for the Sake of the Kids*?

   ______________________________

   ______________________________

   ______________________________

   ______________________________

   In what way do you identify with the importance of the statistical data reported in this article as it relates to your own children?

   ______________________________

   ______________________________

   ______________________________

   ______________________________

2. What insights from Chapter 2 of *Blended Families* were most helpful to you?

   ______________________________

   ______________________________

   ______________________________

   ______________________________

3. Reflect for a moment on Mother Teresa's words: "I have come more and more to realize that it is being unwanted that is the worst disease that any human being can ever experience. Nowadays we have found medicine for leprosy, and lepers can be cured. There's medicine for TB, and consumption can be cured. For all kinds of diseases there are medicines and cures. But for being unwanted, except there are willing hands to serve and there's a loving heart to love, I don't think this terrible disease can be cured." [2]

   What does this quote mean to you?

   ______________________________

   ______________________________

   ______________________________

   ______________________________

4. How could Mother Teresa's words be applied to your family? Be specific.

5. At the bottom of page 40 in the *Blended Families* book is a paragraph that talks about our first major breakthrough in shedding our naiveté. What was that breakthrough?

   After coming to grips with this breakthrough perspective, what new decision did we have to make?

   How have you and your partner chosen to accept this same truth about your family?

6. Make a chart of each family member. Beneath their names, list their position in the family and a perceived need in their lives. Include yourself. (Page 39–40 of *Blended Families* will help you start.)

   Name ________________

   Position: ____________________

   Need: ______________________________________________

Name ________________

Position: _____________________

Need: _________________________________________________________

Name ________________

Position: _____________________

Need: _________________________________________________________

Name ________________

Position: _____________________

Need: _________________________________________________________

Name ________________

Position: _____________________

Need: _________________________________________________________

Name ________________

Position: _____________________

Need: _________________________________________________________

Name ________________

Position: _____________________

Need: _________________________________________________________

Name ________________

Position: _____________________

Need: _________________________________________________________

7. As much as it depends on you, what can be done to meet the perceived need (that you recorded above) for each one of your family members?

   My partner: ______________________________

   Myself: ______________________________

   1st Child: ______________________________

   2nd Child: ______________________________

   3rd Child: ______________________________

   4th Child: ______________________________

   5th Child: ______________________________

   6th Child: ______________________________

8. Adoption is only one way some couples choose to make their families appear more blended and lessen the two-surname embarrassment they might possibly be feeling. What choices, if any, did your family make (with good intentions) to ease the awkwardness of blended living?

   ______________________________

   ______________________________

   ______________________________

   ______________________________

   What were the results of these choices?

   ______________________________

   ______________________________

   ______________________________

   ______________________________

   How did these decisions impact other family members?

   ______________________________

9. An important step in blending is to define your blended family. Turn to page 42–43 of *Blended Families*. Both you and your partner have satellite family members. Explain what a satellite family is made up of.

10. Make a chart listing the members of your extended satellite groupings. Satellite A represents the man's relatives, both natural and ex. Satellite B represents the woman's relatives, both natural and ex.

| **Satellite A** | **Satellite B** |
| --- | --- |
| | |

11. Once more, let's turn our thoughts to the children. Give several reasons why it would benefit your children to have an ongoing relationship with the relatives you named on the above satellite charts.

How have you encouraged these relationships?

12. Are there valid reasons why you should not encourage relationships between some of these satellite individuals and your children? Who might that be and why?

What have you done to keep your children from being involved with these people?

13. Write out Galatians 5:13–15. Underline the words *free* and *freedom*. Circle the two commands given for the proper use of our freedom in Christ. Next, highlight the phrase that sums up the entire law of God.

Who is your neighbor?

What will happen to us if we fail to love others as our neighbor?

Do you have difficulty with this truth of Scripture? Explain.

14. Why might it be a distasteful thought to treat some people as your neighbor?

15. If you were to see satellite family members as your neighbors, how would that affect the blending of your families?

**A Reflective Moment**

Love is such an important part of Your character, Lord. Bring to our minds how important it is to be a giver of love, even when we don't feel like it or those people around us aren't easily lovable. You still expect us to love our neighbor in obedience to Your word, and as we would want to be loved ourselves. You've even promised us blessings when we show love and warned of unhappy consequences when we don't.

We've come to understand that a big part of loving our family means that we care about meeting each person's primary needs. The truth is if we're genuinely attentive to those we live with we will discover wonderful ways to bless them. Grant us the ability to care deeply for our family.

**Practical Application for next week's lesson: Turn to pages 127–132 of the Workbook Enhancement Pages. Allow enough time to complete the *Personality Profile* and the *Enrich Your Relationship* page.**

# WEEK THREE

## *Maximizing Your Marriage*

*Submit to one another out of reverence for Christ.*

Ephesians 5:21

*When words are many, sin is not absent, but he who holds his tongue is wise. . . . The lips of the righteous know what is fitting, but the mouth of the wicked only what is perverse.*

Proverbs 10:19,32

> Henceforth there will be such a oneness between us—that when one weeps the other will taste salt.
>
> —Author Unknown

**Read Chapter 3 of *Blended Families: Build a Primary Unit***

1. What two thoughts meant the most to you from Chapter 3 of *Blended Families*?

   1. ____________________

   2. ____________________

2. Write out Genesis 2:18.

   ____________________

What human need did God intend to meet with this statement?

3. Read Genesis 2:22–25. Describe what you think God means when He says, "They will become one flesh."

   Does this one-flesh concept seem possible to you? Why or why not?

4. How does the biblical look at marriage differ from the worldly perspective of marriage?

5. Read Genesis 1:27. We are told in this verse that God created man in His image. Here the word *man* refers to both the male and female gender. How does it make you feel to think of a God-created equality with shared responsibilities between men and women?

What instructions did God give to the couple?

6. Look at your personality profile. What is your dominant personality type?

   What is your partner's dominant personality type?

   Why is it important to understand both your personality strengths as well as your personality weaknesses?

7. Take five minutes for people to talk about their "Enrich Your Relationship" pages. Instruct couples to face each other and share their answers. Encourage singles to discuss their answers with another single or with a leader. Answer the question: How

can understanding our individual personality strengths and weaknesses help us to resolve the problems we wrote down on this sheet?

8. In marriage, God unites our lives, both the differences and the similarities. List some of the qualities you both brought into the relationship (i.e. one a spender, one a saver, one compassionate, one is prone to impatience).

9. How might God have meant for a family to benefit when spouses with opposite personality traits pull together in appreciation of their differences?

10. In what way have you sometimes found your differences made it difficult for you to communicate with your partner?

11. Look at page 53 of *Blended Families*. What was the substance God used to form a man?

______________________________________________

______________________________________________

How did this differ from the way he formed a woman?

______________________________________________

______________________________________________

______________________________________________

______________________________________________

12. Continue reading to page 54. A husband who competes with his wife ________ a ____________ against himself.

Adam looked at Eve as _______ of his _______ and flesh of his _________. Does this view of marriage describe what's happening in your home? Why or why not?

______________________________________________

______________________________________________

______________________________________________

______________________________________________

13. Read Genesis 2:24. (Refer to page 60–64 of *Blended Families*) What does it mean to leave and cleave?

______________________________________________

______________________________________________

______________________________________________

______________________________________________

Describe how you have left your father and mother and are cleaving to your spouse.

______________________________________________

______________________________________________

______________________________________________

______________________________________________

Describe the additional leaving and cleaving that needs to be done, as it relates to your ex spouse, when you are remarried.

14. When blending two families into one, it helps to see the new family structure as a business venture. In effect, a new corporation has been formed. Be honest. How well are you living up to the bylaws of your corporation? (Support payments, visitation schedules, other items written in the divorce decree.)

What is your greatest frustration with these bylaws?

15. Name the assets held by the shareholders of your newly formed family.

Who sits on the family's board of directors, and who are the shareholders?

16. (From page 64) Even though our children come from a fragmented family, they can grow up emotionally whole if we ___________ our "business affairs" ___________.

17. Read 1 Corinthians 16:13–14. Name five things you can do to best protect the family's assets.

    1. ________________________________________
    2. ________________________________________
    3. ________________________________________
    4. ________________________________________
    5. ________________________________________

### A Reflective Moment

We are so blessed to be different by design. The biggest reason to appreciate our differences is because there are so many little eyes watching us do this thing called marriage. It really matters that children see good examples. With Your help, Lord, alongside a spirit of humility, we can be the husband and wife you want us to be. We can even respect those we are no longer married to, and as much as it depends on us, choose to co-parent with cooperation. When there is jealousy and disagreement, give us hearts to trust, hands to serve, and ears to listen. May our differences produce incentives to celebrate, not grounds to inflict pain.

**Practical Application for next week's lesson: Turn to page 133 of the Workbook Enhancement Pages and complete the sheet *Effective Communication: Why Body Language is so Important.***

# WEEK FOUR

# *The Importance of the Past*

*No one can really know what anyone else is thinking, or what he is really like, except that person himself.*

1 Corinthians 2:11a

*Therefore, if anyone is in Christ, he is a new creation; the old has gone, the new has come!*

2 Corinthians 5:17

> And I am hard-pressed to recognize my self-serving ploys. In a meadow of lupine, with a full belly and a calendar empty of appointments, I convince myself of sainthood. It is community that finds me out. My family, constituents, neighbors—these are the tillers of my soul.[3]

**Read Chapter 4 of *Blended Families: Let's Look Back***

1. What meant the most to you after reading Chapter 4 of *Blended Families*?

______________________________________________

______________________________________________

______________________________________________

______________________________________________

2. Why is it so important to tune into body language as a major form of communication?

______________________________________________

______________________________________________

______________________________________________

______________________________________________

3. Is it ever fair to assume to know what another person will think or feel? Why?

______________________________________________

______________________________________________

______________________________________________

______________________________________________

The next time a family issue is discussed, will you give your mate an opportunity to tell you how he or she feels rather than forming your own opinion? _____

How could these skills improve your communication?

______________________________________________

______________________________________________

______________________________________________

______________________________________________

4. God desires truth from His children. (Psalm 51:6) Do you struggle with honesty? Why is it important to be honest with ourselves and with one another?

______________________________________________

______________________________________________

______________________________________________

______________________________________________

Complete the statements:

If I were to tell my spouse (or partner) how I really feel about being a stepparent, I think he or she would:

______________________________________________

If I were to tell my spouse (or partner) how I really feel about no longer being the custodial parent of my biological child, I think my spouse would:

5. Turn to page 75 of *Blended Families*: Revisiting the past—even unpleasant memories and discoveries—is a ____________. Why is this true?

6. List six reasons found on page 76 that might explain why God allows us to see our past as snapshots of who we are.

   1. ______
   2. ______
   3. ______
   4. ______
   5. ______
   6. ______

7. Is there something in your family's history you'd rather not revisit? Will you ask God to give you courage to move ahead?

Are you willing to look at your own historical identity with a spirit of adventure, not fear of discovery? _________ Will you do the same for your partner? _________

8. Begin to chart your own historical identity. Childhood influences and environment play important roles, forming the threads that shape your adult life. Page 81 in *Blended Families* will help you get started.

   My story:

9. With an open spirit of adventure and discovery, *not* of poking fun or ridicule, compare your history to that of your partner. Summarize the similarities and the differences the two of you discovered.

10. In what way do you have a deeper appreciation, more understanding, and greater empathy for your partner after talking about your individual histories?

______________________________________________

______________________________________________

______________________________________________

______________________________________________

What would you say are your most complementary qualities as a couple? (i.e. she takes personal responsibility and he forgives quickly; he saves and she budgets wisely.)

______________________________________________

______________________________________________

______________________________________________

______________________________________________

Was anything discovered that was previously unknown or that dug up a hurtful memory that needs to be taken to the Lord in prayer?

______________________________________________

______________________________________________

______________________________________________

______________________________________________

11. Generational sins leave their mark on a family. How well do you understand your own family's generational sins? Read Exodus 20:5. What is God talking about in this verse? Turn to page 86 of *Blended Families*.

______________________________________________

______________________________________________

______________________________________________

______________________________________________

12. Generational sins are not unusual. They are common. As you recorded your personal histories, did you unveil any generational sins (i.e. bitterness, neglect of prayer, anger, substance abuse, critical spirit . . .) that need to be dealt with? ____

Describe these problematic behaviors.

Why is it important to clean these things up?

Write out a prayer that, as God enables you, reflects your desire to stop your family's generational sins in your generation.

13. How well do you accept the unique history of your blended children? Their roots include natural qualities inherited from another parent—now an ex-spouse.

How could appreciation, rather than resentment, of the historical origin of each child be helpful to your family?

14. If your children were asked to describe your marriage, would they say they see a couple who is pulling together on the same team, or do they witness a competitive game of tug-of-war between the two of you?

_______________

_______________

_______________

_______________

15. Blended families have the greatest potential to be conflict-ridden homes. We not only have the usual conflicts within the family under our roof, we also have extra tension brought in by the two other families our respective children are a part of. To what degree do the other parent figures affect the dynamics of your home?

_______________

_______________

_______________

_______________

**A Reflective Moment**

Not one of us was created by chance. We are each designer originals, thought of by You before we ever spent a single day in our mother's womb. You chose the time when we would be born and who our parents would be. Sometimes it's hard to make sense of the memories of our past, but we pray for the ability to accept even the painful things about ourselves and our family members.

Through the Scriptures we learn that everyone experiences pain and joy during his or her lifetime. Knowing that You, Jesus, experienced pain too brings many things into perspective. And it helps to know Your relatives, like Abraham and David, didn't always make the right choices. And your great-great-great grandmother, Rahab, was far from being seen as the upper crust of society. They were all sinners in need of a savior. You weren't looking for perfection in these people, You were looking for faith. May our faith grow in greater measure as we walk with You from day-to-day.

**Practical Application for next week's lesson: Turn to page 135 of the Workbook Enhancement Pages. Read '*Keep A-Goin,*' and answer the questions.**

# WEEK FIVE

## *Anger Amongst Us*

*Do not be quickly provoked in your spirit, for anger resides in the lap of fools.*
Ecclesiastes 7:9

*A hot-tempered man stirs up dissension, but a patient man calms a quarrel.*
Proverbs 15:18

> Anger is a habit—a temperament-induced, sinful habit—ignited through the years by distresses and unpleasant circumstances that can control a person as tenaciously as heroin or cocaine, making him react inwardly or outwardly in a selfish, sinful manner. Unless you let the power of God within you change your thinking patterns, your condition will gradually ruin your health, mind, business, family, or spiritual maturity. In addition, it grieves the Holy Spirit (Ephesians 4:30–31), robbing you of the abundant life that Jesus Christ wants to give you.[4]

**Read Chapter 5 of *Blended Families: When Anger Rules***

1. Share your thoughts from the poem, *Keep A-Goin*, with the rest of your class.

___

___

___

______________________________________________

2. What did you find the most interesting after reading Chapter 5, *When Anger Rules*?

______________________________________________

______________________________________________

______________________________________________

______________________________________________

3. Did you previously know that anger is always a secondary emotion? ___
Anger can cover up deeper feelings of rejection, loss, suppressed grief, or failure. Take a moment to reflect on your life. Identify, as best you can, those areas where anger might be covering up a secondary emotion.

______________________________________________

______________________________________________

______________________________________________

______________________________________________

4. From Gary Jackson Oliver and H. Norman Wright's quote near the bottom of page 93 of *Blended Families*, we learn that anger is a ______________ part of close relationships.

What are the two things these men say attracts us to one another? (page 94)

1. ______________________________________________

2. ______________________________________________

In the next paragraph of page 93, we are told anger-energy communicates two things. What are those two things?

1. ______________________________________________

2. ______________________________________________

5. Think of three or four qualities that initially attracted you to your partner.

______________________________________________

______________________________________________

______________________________________________

Do you still appreciate these qualities? Or, do these same qualities now prove to be an irritation to you?

6. Read Genesis 4:5b–7. What role did anger play in Cain's life?

   How did God respond to Cain's anger?

   According to the wisdom found in James 4:1–3, what causes quarrels among us?

7. On page 99 of *Blended Families* there is a quote from David Seamands, author of *Putting Away Childish Things*. He brings us face-to-face with childish behaviors that we've carried along into our adult lives. He wrote:

   *The little child of the past makes himself most clearly known in the place where a child is most comfortable—the home, and in those personal contacts and relationships which feel most like home. The hardest place to live maturely is with close friends, a roommate, a sweetheart, and colleagues at work and with family. For the little child tends to take over in close relationships.*[5]

Be as transparent as possible and describe how your anger might be taking on childish characteristics in close relationships at home and at work (i.e. tantrums, name calling, silence, throwing objects).

8. Personal: Reflect on a time when your anger created a major problem.

How did others react to your anger?

Were you able to resolve the problem? How?

9. What is the four-step battle plan to resist destructive anger described on pages 97–101 of *Blended Families*?

1. 

2. 

3. ______________________________
4. ______________________________

10. What ticks you off? List your anger trigger points. Why are these so important to know?

______________________________

______________________________

______________________________

______________________________

11. Page 98 of *Blended Families* shows four arrows that make known a downward progression typical of unhealthy anger. What do these four arrows represent?

1. ______________ 2. ______________

3. ______________ 4. ______________

At what point are we able to step off the downward spiral?

______________________________

______________________________

______________________________

______________________________

12. Read Ephesians 4:26–27. How does God expect us to manage our anger?

______________________________

______________________________

______________________________

______________________________

How long are we supposed to stay angry?

______________________________

______________________________

______________________________

______________________________

How long do you typically stay angry?

13. Anger is one of many human emotions. The problem is not the experience of feeling anger. The problem with anger is the direction we allow it to take. Are there times when anger is good? What could be the benefits of good anger?

Can you remember a time when Jesus got angry? How did He behave?

14. Explain how the emotion of anger has the potential to also become an addictive behavior. Why do you think a person would become addicted to anger?

15. Illustrate a current story in the news that fits an example of destructive anger.

As a result of this act of rage, what consequences can you realistically believe will be put in motion for the people directly involved?

16. Do you believe God can forgive your misuse of anger? (1 John 3:9) Have you asked Him to?

17. Personal: Consider writing letters or making phone calls asking forgiveness of those you may have offended with your anger. Begin with family members. Place a check beside the name after you have followed through with this action step..

**A Reflective Moment**

Anger is a powerful and complex secondary emotion. I haven't always thought of it that way. Is it possible that behind my angry facade there's something about me I haven't fully understood; something I don't want others to know?

For the times when angry outbursts have poured fear and sorrow into this family, forgive me, Lord, for the part I've played. Help me find ways to heal those wounds. I would pray for a mouth that speaks from a heart that is ready to say a kind word, instead of a hurtful one. The next time I'm tempted to vent my discontent on someone, may I remember that You want me to be slow to anger and quick to listen. Remind me that anger is only good when it is accompanied by self-control and, according to Your Word, there is never a time when anger has to lead to sin.

By applying spiritual wisdom I can bring maturity to the little child who still lives within my big adult body. I now understand that it is unfair to use others as an excuse to become angry. No one makes me angry. Anger is always a choice I make.

**Practical Application for next week's lesson: Turn to page 136 of the Workbook Enhancement Pages. Read *Effective Discipline*.**

# WEEK SIX

## *Discipline in Love*

*Train a child in the way he should go, and when he is old he will not turn from it.*
Proverbs 22:6

*Fathers, do not exasperate your children, or they will become discouraged.*
Colossians 3:21

*No discipline seems pleasant at the time, but painful. Later on, however, it produces a harvest of righteousness and peace for those who have been trained by it.*
Hebrews 12:11

**A Bag of Tools**

Isn't it strange that princes and kings,
And clowns that caper in sawdust rings,
And common people like you and me
Are builders for eternity?

Each is given a bag of tools,
A shapeless mass, a book of rules;
And each must make—ere life is flown—a
Stumbling block or a stepping stone.[6]

– R. L. Sharpe

**Read Chapter 6 of *Blended Families: Who's In Charge?***

1. What truths did you discover as a result of reading the practical application article, *Effective Discipline*?

___

___

___

___

2. Are you frustrated with the way discipline is being administered within your home? Why or why not?

___

___

___

___

3. Who do you think should be the number one disciplinarian of the children? Give a reason for your answer.

___

___

___

___

4. After reading the opening story of Chapter 6, describe the problems Brent encountered.

___

___

___

___

Why was it unwise for the stepparent to assume the authoritarian role with his stepson so soon after the wedding?

___

Why do you think the mother in this story didn't speak up?

5. How was discipline administered in your home of origin? Are you parenting in a similar way?

6. On pages 109–110 of *Blended Families*, we find two fathers. The *Captain* father and the *Mr. Rogers* father see fatherhood very differently. What are their differences?

| *Captain father* | *Mr. Rogers father* |
| --- | --- |
| | |

7. Men: Which of these two parent figures do you most closely resemble? ___________

   Women: Which of these two parent figures does your husband resemble? ___________

   Both men and women: Which of these two fathers did your own father most closely resemble? _______________

   Think about this same scenario as it pertains to motherhood. Women: Do you most closely parent as the *Captain* mother or the *Mrs. Rogers* mother? _______________

   Men: Which of these parenting styles defines your wife the best? _______________

   Both men and women: In your own childhood, did your mother parent with the *Captain's* style or that of *Mrs. Rogers*? ____________________

8. The root word of discipline is *disciple*. When we think of this word, our minds travel to Jesus and His twelve disciples. These men were followers of Jesus' teachings. With the word *disciple* in mind, and a dictionary as help, write out a definition for the word *discipline*.

   ______________________________________________________________________

   ______________________________________________________________________

   ______________________________________________________________________

   ______________________________________________________________________

9. Jesus did not focus on discipline as a means of punishing people, although consequences do follow disobedience. As shown in Mark 10:35–45 and Matthew 13:1–9, Jesus used discipline as an educational tool to teach specific truths to his disciples. Through effective communication His listeners could easily learn a better choice could be made. How does this awareness about discipline reconstruct your thinking and change the consequences that you will impose upon your children in the future?

   ______________________________________________________________________

   ______________________________________________________________________

   ______________________________________________________________________

   ______________________________________________________________________

10. From page 112 of *Blended Families*, "Discipline is an act of __________, not an opportunity to vent _____________ and impose ______________."

On this same page, we learn that discipline not "meted out in love will have __________ effectiveness and the potential to produce ______________ rather than positive change." Why do you think this is true?

______________________________________________

______________________________________________

______________________________________________

______________________________________________

11. Read Hebrews 12:5–6. Who are the people the Lord disciplines?

______________________________________________

______________________________________________

______________________________________________

______________________________________________

12. Pages 115–116 of *Blended Families* tell a story about the struggles going on in Lynn's family. Her husband's lack of love for her son put their family in a very tough situation. How did that make Lynn feel?

______________________________________________

______________________________________________

______________________________________________

______________________________________________

Have you honestly accepted each of your stepchildren with a heart of love? Do they know for a fact that you love them? If not, why do you think the children feel the way they do?

______________________________________________

______________________________________________

______________________________________________

______________________________________________

13. On a scale of 1–10 (10 being the highest score to achieve), how would you measure the effort you've put into building solid relationships with your stepchildren? ______ Give examples of what you have done to show acceptance to your stepchildren.

______________________________________________

14. If the rules outweigh the relationship between you and your stepchild, do you believe that child will respect you as a disciplinarian? Will your mate respect you? Explain.

15. In Psalm 127:3 God says: "Sons are a heritage from the Lord, children a reward from him." Share below how you either agree or disagree with this verse.

16. Why might parents of children in blended families have a more difficult time administering discipline or being consistent in its use?

17. Discipline within the home is one thing, but discipline between homes is another matter altogether. What are the similarities and differences between the discipline methods in your home and the discipline style used in the home of the other birth parent?

| **Similarities** | **Differences** |
|---|---|
| | |
| | |
| | |
| | |

Describe how these differences have perhaps caused confusion for the child or conflict between the homes.

__________________________________________________________

__________________________________________________________

__________________________________________________________

__________________________________________________________

Think about your child having to live in two different countries with differing governments. In a way, that's what blended children do. They have citizenship in two homes. How can you help your child live with both sets of rules?

__________________________________________________________

__________________________________________________________

__________________________________________________________

__________________________________________________________

18. Sit down with your spouse this week and look at discipline realistically. Make a plan that keeps the familiar patterns in place while slowly incorporating new *blended* discipline concepts to govern the children's behaviors. The goal is to move toward unity in discipline over a longer period of time.

### A Reflective Moment

Perhaps we've moved too fast with this whole discipline thing. We didn't realize how unfair that was to our children. Maybe it's time to slow down, lower our expectations, and take time to respect the discipline the children are already familiar with. As parents, we must remember to focus on giving correction in love and not punishment out of frustration. You have given us a great responsibility to train up these little ones. The last thing we want to do is to take that duty lightly and crush the tender spirit within our sons and daughters.

Our prayer, Lord, is that You will help us to find that space of spousal unity where we can come to an agreement on fair and reasonable consequences for every one of our blended children. And, please grant us an extra measure of understanding to respect the discipline being administered in the homes of our ex partners, and the wisdom to know when there is a real reason not to remain silent. Help our children, Lord. They'll need a greater measure of thoughtfulness in order to respect the rules in both their homes.

**Congratulations! You have now completed Unit One of the *Blended Families Workbook*. Prayerfully consider continuing on and finishing Unit Two as well. Leaders: Remember to sign the Unit One portion of the *Certificate of Completion* for each student. This is found near the back of the workbook. Go to www.blendedfamilies.net to print certificates in color.**

# Unit Two

**Practical Application for week one's lesson: Turn to pages 139–142 of the Workbook Enhancement Pages: Complete the *Youth Personality Profile*, read the *Birth Order* page. Also become familiar with the story, *A Pail of Fresh Berries* on pages 143–144.**

# WEEK ONE

# *Consider the Children*

*Jesus said, "Let the little children come to me, and do not hinder them, for the kingdom of heaven belongs to such as these."*

Matthew 19:14

*Trust in the Lord with all your heart and lean not on your own understanding; in all your ways acknowledge him, and he will make your paths straight.*

Proverbs 3:5–6

> Today the wind invited the children and me outside to chase it. So we did. The trees, like dancing gypsies with jewels in their hair, laughed above us as we frolicked down the street. The pockets of my jacket began to fill with autumn treasures, placed there by two sets of small hands.[7]

**Read Chapter 7 of *Blended Families: Children in the Midst of Change***

1. Every child is born with a bent toward a distinct personality type. As a result of completing the Youth Personality Profile, which of the four personality styles best describes each of your children?

___

___

___

___

How does knowing individual personality information help you understand your child?

2. Change is a big factor for children in blended families. What would you say are the most significant lifestyle changes each of your children has had to make as a result of your decision to remarry?

3. By the time a blended child reaches age eighteen, he or she will most likely have lived in at least four different homes. (1.) The home of origin (2.) The single parent home (3.) The home of a stepfather or stepmother (4.) The home of a close relative or foster parent.

   Explain how a child from a blended family might not feel home represents a stable environment?

   List two or three things a parent can do to be sensitive to the numerous living arrangements a child encounters during these formative years (i.e. wall calendar, permanent dresser drawer, chores for everyone).

4. Childhood grief is a serious matter. When you think of grieving, what word pictures come to mind?

What events have brought grief into your own life? Think back as far as you can.

Turn to pages 125–128 of *Blended Families*. How have you helped each of your blended children resolve grief?

Your child will most likely act out in behaviors rather than tell you why he or she is sad or angry about his or her loss. Are there any new behaviors you've seen in your children since the loss of their prior family?

5. How can you creatively keep the memory of an absentee parent alive? (i.e. scrapbook, mailbox, conversation).

6. Read the story, *A Pail of Fresh Berries*, in the Workbook Enhancement Pages. Imagine each child has two pails given to him or her at birth. Both pails are empty, but not for long. The pails represent two things the child will experience throughout life. One bucket is for blessings received; the other for cow pies given!

**Blessings**  **Cow Pies**

Early childhood memories last a lifetime. Some are good and bring smiles, while others chronicle traumatic accounts of earlier physical or emotional pain. What memories do you have from your own childhood? Did your blessings outweigh the cow pies?

7. Get two pails for each of your children—one for *Blessings* and the other for *Cow Pies*. Let the boys and girls design the artwork on their pails. List some of the blessings you know you've given your child or stepchild. Now, be just as honest, write down some of the cow pies you've given these children.

| *Blessings* | *Cow Pies* |
|---|---|
| | |

8. Think of a blessing someone else has given your child/stepchild. (Teacher, grandparent, friend, neighbor.) Next, bring to mind a hurtful cow pie.

9. After reading about birth order, think about the birth order picture at your house. Who is the first born, the last born, the middle born, or the only born?

______________________________

______________________________

______________________________

______________________________

______________________________

______________________________

Which children share birth order roles?

______________________________

______________________________

______________________________

______________________________

Why might birth order be just as important a piece of the family puzzle as is the personality profile we've already talked about?

10. Think about the birth order your child fits into while in the home of his or her other biological parent. What are the similarities and the differences between households?

Similarities

Differences

In what way do you think a disrupted birth order could be affecting your family?

11. Have you begun holding regular family meetings? ___
If so, how often do you meet? Describe how a typical family meeting at your house is conducted.

If you are not holding family meetings, will you make it a goal to start? Write down a date to begin.

______________________________________________________________________

12. We all need communication skills that negotiate problems. (Page 132 of *Blended Families.*) Name a few good things your children can learn during family meetings that could help them get along with others throughout the rest of their lives (i.e. It's safe to talk about feelings, confront with respect, compromise).

______________________________________________________________________

______________________________________________________________________

______________________________________________________________________

______________________________________________________________________

13. A simple approach works best with family meetings. *Blended Families*, pages 132–133, suggests you approach the meeting with a game mindset. Place two bowls in the middle of the table. One bowl is for **What I Like**. The other bowl is for **What I Don't Like**. Notepaper is in front of each bowl. Each person must put a paper in the **What I Like** bowl before they can put a problem in the **What I Don't Like** bowl. This encourages positive thinking. The *Blessings* and *Cow Pies* pails belonging to the children could also provide current resource topics for family meetings, but only if your child is willing to share these in a more corporate way rather than one-on-one with just Mom or Dad.

From *Blended Families*, list five rules you could put in place that would help to make your family meetings a positive experience.

1. ______________________________________________________________
2. ______________________________________________________________
3. ______________________________________________________________
4. ______________________________________________________________
5. ______________________________________________________________

14. In what ways do your blended children respect what belongs to a step-sibling?

______________________________________________________________________

______________________________________________________________________

______________________________________________________________________

15. Read Matthew 7:12. Define *respect* from this passage.

16. Safety issues are even more serious in the blended family. The lack of biological connectedness presents added issues in the home. Children need to know family represents a safe place. Do your children feel safe in your home?

17. Any form of abuse means a trust has been betrayed. Abusive behaviors are not all the same. From pages 139–142 of the text, identify as many types of abuse as you can.

18. You alone know your family's history as it relates to issues of abuse. *Personal*: Is there reason to be overly cautious when it comes to the safety of any of the children in your care?

Why is it important to behave modestly toward one another? What have you done to make sure this happens in your home?

### A Reflective Moment

This week's lesson brings a clearer perspective to the changes we have dropped into our children's lives as a result of our decisions. Forgive us for the times when we've been too preoccupied with our own agenda to see the hurt or fear in their young eyes.

It helps to have a glimpse into our son's and daughter's personality traits. This information opens a whole new parenting door. There may have been times when we've mistakenly thought a behavior was naughty when in reality our child's response was in line with their unique personality. Help us to know the difference. We'll need wisdom, Lord, to train up these precious children according to the way You have uniquely designed them.

When we think of the blessings and cow pies we can so easily drop into our children's lives, we sure want the blessings to outnumber the cow pies nine-to-one. With Your help, we'll be able to teach good communication skills and problem solving techniques. Most of all, Lord, we want our children to know home is a safe place to be, a place where they will be loved and not mistreated, and a place where healing and camaraderie are found.

**Practical Application for next week's lesson: Turn to pages 145–150 of the Workbook Enhancement Pages. Complete the *Household Budget.* Become familiar with the *Financial Topics for the Blended Family* and *Successful Money Strategies* found here. Highlight those topics that your family needs to discuss more fully.**

# WEEK TWO

## *For Richer—For Poorer*

*Now he who supplies seed to the sower and bread for food will also supply and increase your store of seed and will enlarge the harvest of your righteousness. You will be made rich in every way so that you can be generous on every occasion.*

2 Corinthians 9:10–11a

> Money is not for spending. It is for managing first and then for spending. . . . When money flows into your life, you are responsible for its performance. You are the composer, the concertmaster, and the conductor. You direct that money according to the score you have written. [8]

**Read Chapter 8 of *Blended Families: The Impact of Money***

1. Money is a very touchy subject. What did you find most interesting in Chapter 8?

____________________________________________

____________________________________________

____________________________________________

____________________________________________

After doing the Household Budget Worksheet, how do you feel about your family's finances? What is the biggest concern? How do you plan to address this issue?

How I feel: ______

The greatest concern: ______

The plan: ______

2. See page 164 of *Blended Families*. Why do people avoid making a budget?

   1. ______
   2. ______
   3. ______

3. Why is it healthy for a budget to be flexible?

______

______

4. How well did you understand your partner's financial picture prior to your wedding day? Did financial surprises surface after the wedding?

______

______

______

______

5. *Personal*: Were the two of you from a background of similar economic means, or were you more lopsided, like Chapter 8's opening story of Jim and Linda?

______

______

6. Describe how the two of you worked out a plan that would pull your combined finances together to meet the needs of your newly blended family?

______

______

______

______

Did your plan take into consideration the needs of both former families? How?

7. Remarriage has the potential to bring in messy inheritance problems. Read page 155 of the text. What was Julia's concern?

How could this parent have made his daughter feel more at ease?

Are there any heartfelt items or heirlooms from your prior relationship that your children feel a special attachment to? How have you handled this problem?

8. Many blended families put off making a will. Why might this be?

Have you drawn up a will? Why is it important to have a will?

9. What arrangements have you made for the care of your minor children in the event of your unexpected death, supposing your child's other biological parent has either preceded you in death or would be unavailable to care for the children?

At the time your prior mate died or divorce occurred, had you made preplanned funeral arrangements for yourself? If so, has remarriage changed your plans? How have you communicated these changes to your children?

10. Is money good or bad? What does it mean to love money? (1 Timothy 6:10).

11. What hardships might happen to your family if your ex, or your partner's ex, takes you back to court for increased child support? Do you have a plan for financial survival should this happen?

12. For those who remarried after divorce, have you thought about the debts you left behind? Are you still in a shared liability with a debt you thought was given to your ex by your divorce decree? Read the statement below. Underneath that statement describe how you have resolved the financial obligations you once had with your ex.

> Divorce means we split up everything, including the debts; however, the debts are not easily split. If your name is on a debt, you are liable to pay it, and your credit is affected if you don't. A divorce court does not have the power to take your name off a debt. The divorce judge only has the power to tell your spouse to pay it for you. If your spouse doesn't pay, you can tell the judge, but you are still liable. [9]

13. To train a child to handle money, a child has to *have* money. In your home, how do the children get money to spend?

14. What is the meaning of delayed gratification?

Can you think of a time when you chose to put off buying an item until you had saved up the money, rather than going into debt? What was the result of this decision?

15. Name the three basic money principles you can teach your son or daughter by giving him or her three jars. Look at page 167.

    1. ______
    2. ______
    3. ______

16. How has debt affected your family?

    If you are in debt, do you have a plan to get out of debt? Describe that plan.

17. Estimate the amount of money your family spends on entertainment each month.

    $______.

    Share a couple reasons why it's important to keep fun in the household budget.

    1. ______
    2. ______

    Make a list of the activities your family enjoys doing together.

18. Children learn by example. Think back to your childhood. How did your parents manage their money?

______________________________________________________________________________

______________________________________________________________________________

______________________________________________________________________________

______________________________________________________________________________

How well were you equipped to make good financial decisions when you graduated high school? Did you have your own checking or savings account?

______________________________________________________________________________

______________________________________________________________________________

______________________________________________________________________________

______________________________________________________________________________

19. Be honest in naming the ways in which your current spending habits are similar to those you observed in your childhood home.

______________________________________________________________________________

______________________________________________________________________________

______________________________________________________________________________

______________________________________________________________________________

20. Does money cause you to lie awake at night? What kinds of money problems interrupt your rest?

______________________________________________________________________________

______________________________________________________________________________

______________________________________________________________________________

______________________________________________________________________________

Is there something you can do about your finances that would be proactive and more productive than worrying?

______________________________________________________________________________

______________________________________________________________________________

______________________________________________________________________________

______________________________________________________________________________

21. Write out Philippians 4:6–7. Underline God's instructions. Circle His promise.

______________________________________________

______________________________________________

______________________________________________

______________________________________________

### A Reflective Moment

The world might be a happier place if we didn't have to spend so much time thinking about money. Since that's not a realistic thought, Lord, we need Your wisdom to develop a budget that will work for our family. On those occasions when something unexpected happens and our bills suddenly seem to outnumber the sum of our paycheck, help us to remember we're not alone. You've already promised to meet our needs. Rather than getting upset or feeling defeated, lead us to respond with prayer and faith.

It's so hard to talk about writing a will, but we know this is an important part of responsible parenting. Because we want what's fair and reasonable for our combined children, we'll need clarity in seeking out good legal counsel to effectively complete this task with the least amount of confusion and disagreement. Keep it foremost in our minds that our relationships with people are the real riches of Your Kingdom and the stuff of this world will all be left behind.

In humility, and with full knowledge that money can influence both good and bad decisions, we boldly ask for a hedge of protection around our family. When thoughts of greed and selfishness tempt us to step off the right path, remind us that our children are learning financial habits by the example we set. We pray that they learn to be responsible spenders, generous givers, and purposeful savers, who are not prone to love money more than people.

**Practical Application for next week's lesson: Do two things this week:**

1. **Write a prayer for your family's finances and make time to share this prayer with your partner.**
2. **Make plans (and set a date) for a fun day together as a family. Form the plan and determine how much money will be needed for this activity.**

My Prayer

______________________________________________

______________________________________________

______________________________________________

My Plans for a Fun Day

These Plans will Cost $ _______

# WEEK THREE

# Feelings of Guilt and Shame

*The ransomed of the Lord will return. They will enter Zion with singing; everlasting joy will crown their heads. Gladness and joy will overtake them, and sorrow and sighing will flee away.*

Isaiah 51:11

> Kids need to know their parents think they're number one, whether they're 21 years old or 21 days old. . . . there is a legitimate self-esteem that we must work to instill in our children. If a child knows he is loved, if a child is disciplined, if a child is protected, if a child is made to do his chores, he will have the right kind of self-esteem, and not the synthetic type offered by the liberal experts of our day.[10]

**Read Chapter 9 of *Blended Families: The Influence of Guilt and Shame***

1. Did you take time to write your financial prayer and share it with your partner? _____
   Share the fun you planned with the class.

2. After reading Chapter 9, did you find that guilt and shame have played a part in the past or are now playing an active role in your life? Personal: What memories of guilt and shame are the most vivid for you?

________________________________________

________________________________________

________________________________________

________________________________________

Up until now how have you dealt with your feelings of guilt and shame? (i.e. denial, anger, blame, alcohol, or . . . .).

________________________________________

________________________________________

________________________________________

________________________________________

3. People invent many ways to escape their shame. None of them work. They only push the shame out the front door of their feelings and let it in again through the back door. The better way to deal with shame is to not escape it but to heal it. [11]

   Why might this be true?

________________________________________

________________________________________

________________________________________

________________________________________

4. Try to explain the different ways guilt played a significant role in the opening story of Chapter 9.

________________________________________

________________________________________

________________________________________

________________________________________

Why didn't Alan feel free to talk about his feelings of guilt?

___

___

___

___

5. There is a quote by Dr. Minirth at the bottom of page 182. In your own words, describe Dr. Minirth's definition of the beautiful side of guilt.

___

___

___

___

Have you ever experienced a time when you realized God was using the beautiful side of guilt to remove some of your rough edges?

___

___

___

___

6. Page 184 of *Blended Families* tells of two pathways one can take with guilt. Each path has six steps. What will be encountered on each path?

| *Pathway One* ↑ | *Pathway Two* ↓ |
| --- | --- |
| *1.* | 1. |
| *2.* | 2. |
| *3.* | 3. |
| *4.* | 4. |
| *5.* | 5. |
| *6.* | 6. |

7. Which pathway can you most easily identify with?

_______________

_______________

_______________

_______________

8. How is the power of conviction different from the heaviness of guilt?

_______________

_______________

_______________

_______________

Who is the true author of conviction? Why would this gift be given to us?

_______________

_______________

_______________

_______________

9. Shame is a deeper problem. The same initial guilt is felt, but guilt feelings soon turn to self-disgust and shame. A person filled with shame feels like a __________. The action isn't the problem; ______ is (page 186 of *Blended Families*).

10. Shame-filled people mistakenly look at themselves as loathsome people, not respectable people. With that mindset, how do you think shame and addictive behaviors (alcohol, drugs, etc.) feed on one another?

_______________

_______________

_______________

_______________

11. What does it mean to have a shame-centered marriage?

_______________

_______________

_______________

_______________

12. Go to page 191 of *Blended Families*. Psychological shame causes people to be hypersensitive about what others _________ and ______ about them. They have a great need to be ____________ acceptable.

    Could this statement be true of you? Why?

    ______________________________________________

    ______________________________________________

    ______________________________________________

    ______________________________________________

    Have you experienced times when you had a false sense of shame based on negative comments you heard from the people you cared the most about? These messages are one of Satan's ploys intended to create low self-esteem. How did the actions of these individuals affect you?

    ______________________________________________

    ______________________________________________

13. While some shame originates in genuine guilt, it is also possible to take on someone else's shame. Has a close relative or a co-worker ever caused you public embarrassment (arrested, lied, maybe had an affair, or had a baby out of wedlock . . .)?

    ______________________________________________

    ______________________________________________

    ______________________________________________

    ______________________________________________

14. Life is full of actions followed by reactions. Do the consequences to some of the events of your life feel like a never-ending punishment or do they seem like a natural, yet unpleasant, response to what has taken place?

    ______________________________________________

    ______________________________________________

    ______________________________________________

    ______________________________________________

15. Read Romans 8:1–2. Is it possible to be free from guilt? What words of freedom are found in this passage of Scripture?

    ______________________________________________

_______________________________________________

What action does it take to be in Christ Jesus?

_______________________________________________

_______________________________________________

Have you ever asked Jesus into your heart? ________

16. If you struggle with feelings of guilt because you really have wronged someone, you are under conviction. God is just trying to get your attention. Write out 1 John 1:9. Have you asked Jesus to forgive you?

_______________________________________________

_______________________________________________

_______________________________________________

_______________________________________________

17. Mark Twain once said, "Forgiveness is the fragrance the violet sheds on the heel that has crushed it." Is there someone you need to go to and ask for forgiveness? Ask the Lord to lead you in making a list of the people you need to talk to.

_______________________________________________

_______________________________________________

_______________________________________________

_______________________________________________

Read the Lord's Prayer found in Matthew 6:9–15. What principle, spoken to us by the Lord himself, is the basis for receiving forgiveness?

_______________________________________________

_______________________________________________

What happens when we fail to forgive others?

_______________________________________________

_______________________________________________

18. Think about your testimony to others. How might those who are not Christians be affected by Christian friends or co-workers whose lives are consumed by guilt and shame?

______________________________________________

______________________________________________

______________________________________________

______________________________________________

______________________________________________

______________________________________________

**A Reflective Moment**

I've spent so much time feeling bad about past choices and too many hours concerned about what others have done to me. Real guilt and false guilt have been big issues in my life. Forgive me, Lord, for acting as though what You did on the cross wasn't enough to take away my guilt.

As a result of this week's lesson, I see things differently. I have a deeper understanding of the price You paid to set me free. You are like the artist who so carefully brings about his masterpiece. I am the canvas, eager for the finishing touches to be applied.

What a relief to know You loved me when I felt the least lovable. You didn't expect me to be perfect. That was my expectation. You knew I was a work in process. My hope is that Your work in me will produce spiritual fruit that I can share with my family. I want all of them to know that there's no reason to keep feeling weighed down with the guilt and shame from the past. Freedom is only a prayer away. Thank You, Jesus!

**Practical Application for next week's lesson: Follow up this lesson with any forgiveness letters you need to write or phone calls you need to make.**

# WEEK FOUR

## *Choose a Happy Ending*

*Shout for joy to the Lord, all the earth. Serve the Lord with gladness; come before him with joyful songs. Know that the Lord is God. It is he who made us, and we are his; we are his people, the sheep of his pasture. Enter his gates with thanksgiving and his courts with praise; give thanks to him and praise his name. For the Lord is good and his love endures forever; his faithfulness continues through all generations.*

Psalms 100

> Jesus said, "Do to others as you would have them do to you" (Luke 6:31) [The Golden Rule]. To apply the Golden Rule at your house might mean leaving the bathroom clean for the next person who wants to use it, taking out the garbage without being asked, watching a younger child so your wife can have time with a friend, making your husband's favorite meal, helping with school homework, acknowledging the good qualities in each other, sharing your things with a happy attitude, taking time to listen, praying for one another, or choosing to overlook an offense. The list is unlimited.

**Read Chapter 10 of *Blended Families: Armed With Attitude***

1. Did you write any letters asking for forgiveness or offering forgiveness? What were your feelings after following through with this step?

______________________________________________

2. After reading Chapter 10 of *Blended Families*, why do you think attitude is such a big factor in blended family survival?

3. Two daughters, two attitudes are in the opening story of Chapter 10. Compare the differences in Andrea's and Sabrina's attitudes.

   Why do you think they didn't share the same feelings about our family?

4. How would the people who know you best describe your outlook on life?

5. What eight attitudes did Jesus say would bring us blessings? Matthew 5:3–12

   1.
   2.

3. ____________________
4. ____________________
5. ____________________
6. ____________________
7. ____________________
8. ____________________

6. Which of these attitudes are you already doing a good job with?

Which attitudes do you struggle with the most?

What blessings has God promised us if we live out these attitudes?

Have you already received some of these blessings in your life?

7. From a dictionary, define the word *humble*. Why is it important to be humble?

____________________________________________

____________________________________________

____________________________________________

____________________________________________

8. Fill in the blank from the information found at the bottom of page 208.

   To be ____________, all of life's relationships must have a core ___________ of humility. Without humility of heart, we are ______________________ the master of ______________.

9. Why is receiving encouragement so important to our personal well being?

____________________________________________

____________________________________________

____________________________________________

____________________________________________

10. Page 212 of *Blended Families* informs us of the effects of negative speech. Identify several ways that discouraging words damage a child or a spouse.

____________________________________________

____________________________________________

____________________________________________

____________________________________________

    Is there hurtful language taking place in your home? In what way do you contribute to its use?

____________________________________________

____________________________________________

____________________________________________

____________________________________________

11. Read Larry and Donna's story more closely (page 215–216). By seeking counsel for his frustrations, what new thoughts did Larry discover about being an effective step-parent?

________________________________________

________________________________________

________________________________________

________________________________________

Do you struggle with some of the same things as Larry did? How are you handling your frustrations?

________________________________________

________________________________________

________________________________________

________________________________________

12. Look at Charles Swindoll's quote on page 220. In what way does reading this quote change your thinking about your own attitude?

________________________________________

________________________________________

________________________________________

________________________________________

**A Reflective Moment**

We must realize the need to pray for God-centered attitudes. The way we react to life's events is far more dependent on attitude than on circumstances. Attitudes without constant care can so easily become negative companions. What a blessing to know each reaction acted out in response to a problem is a matter of personal choice. No one else forces an attitude on us. Lord, we would ask that You help us to willingly display humility in place of pride within our family. And we pray specifically that we'd be quick to replace any temptation to use hurtful language towards our family with words of encouragement instead.

**Practical Application for next week's lesson: Go to page 151–153 of the Workbook Enhancement Pages. Complete the *Thoughts to Ponder* pages.**

## WEEK FIVE

# Discovering Hidden Truths

*Who is like the wise man? Who knows the explanation of things? Wisdom brightens a man's face and changes its hard appearance.*

Ecclesiastes 8:1

Parents are the main support anchors in a child's life; when the child feels cared for and loved it reduces the stress level, improves immune function, and produces a healthier adulthood.[12]

**Read Chapter 11 of *Blended Families: One More Blessing***

1. Share with the class your *Thoughts to Ponder* page.

2. Chapter 11 of *Blended Families* talks about relationships that have been more estranged than familiar. A child meets her father for the first time. Page 232 has a poem that talks of just such a meeting. What did the author of this poem discover about herself when she saw her father for the first time?

_______________

_______________

_______________

_______________

3. Think about your own children. What words could your boys and girls write down to illustrate the characteristics they have in common with you?

4. How are you celebrating your families ethnic histories?

   If you are not already doing this, what creative ideas could you begin to implement with your family?

5. In sharing our own story of discovering another daughter, what was Deborah's goal?

   How did her goal differ from ours?

6. What is closure? Why is it necessary in healthy relationships? (See page 234 of *Blended Families.*)

Read John 8:32. What did Jesus say about truth? How can finding out the truth about who you are lead to freedom and closure?

7. Are there things in your past that need to be put in perspective? Do you need to find closure for anything or does your present family live with ghosts from your prior family?

   Write down the steps you have taken to resolve your past.

   Were your efforts appreciated or did they create a greater grief for you or someone else? Why do you think that was?

8. Describe the *ghost* moments. (Those things that consume your thoughts about past relationships and rob you of the ability to enjoy your present family as you should.)

9. Turn to page 238 of *Blended Families*. Fill in the blanks. We like what feels ______________. But we can feel ____________________ with ________________ patterns too.

   What does it mean to you to feel like a *victim*?

   ________________________________________________________________

   ________________________________________________________________

10. How would thinking of yourself as a survivor rather than a victim change things?

   ________________________________________________________________

   ________________________________________________________________

   ________________________________________________________________

   ________________________________________________________________

11. Is life fair? __ Do we as Christians have victory over the things that aren't fair? ____

   Write a verse from Scripture that encourages you to believe you have victory. Romans 8:28 and 8:31 are often favorite verses: *We know that in all things God works for the good of those who love Him. . . . If God is for us, who can be against us?*

   ________________________________________________________________

   ________________________________________________________________

   ________________________________________________________________

   ________________________________________________________________

Take time to commit your chosen verse to memory.

### A Reflective Moment

Thank you for each and every one of our unique ethnic backgrounds. You made no mistake with our DNA. When our sons and daughters look at us, may they feel privileged to share the cultural history that identifies them as "our" children. Equip us with the desire to model positive traits that are worthy of creating a healthy self-esteem in their generation. Our goal is to do our best to live giving respect and honor to each one's ethnicity, not to demean anyone's cultural history. Hold our tongues should we even think to speak a racial slur or utter a debasing comment toward a stepchild, stepparent, stepsibling—or even our ex. This type of language is unbecoming a child of the King.

Where closure is needed please give us the courage to move ahead in spite of the response we might receive from the other person. Help us to lay to rest any unfinished pain from the past and live victoriously with our family.

**Practical Application for next week's lesson. Go to page 155 of the Workbook Enhancement Pages. Complete the *Evaluation Sheet* and give it to your leader next week.**

# WEEK SIX

## *The Fruitful Family*

*Praise the Lord. Praise God in his sanctuary; praise him in his mighty heavens. Praise him for his acts of power; praise him for his surpassing greatness.*

Psalms 150: 1–2

> Getting honest with ourselves does not make us unacceptable to God. It does not distance us from God, but draws us to Him—as nothing else can—and opens us anew to the flow of grace. [13]

**Read Chapter 12 of *Blended Families: Making the Best of It* together with the book's final pages, *A Closing Perspective***

1. In the opening story of Chapter 12, the author found a T-shirt in a store window. What words were printed on the shirt? Why did this particular shirt interest her?

   ______________________________________________

   ______________________________________________

   ______________________________________________

   ______________________________________________

2. Do you have trouble getting over it? Why?

___

___

___

___

Do you wish other people would get over it? Why?

___

___

___

___

3. On page 244 of *Blended Families* a discovery was made.
. . . I figured out I couldn't thank _____ and feel ___________ for myself at the same time.

In what way does this statement support your own experience?

___

___

___

___

4. Juvenile arrests for homicide rose a whopping eight percent between 1980 and 1990 (page 245). What one thing was found to be the most significant reason for the increase in juvenile crime committed by young men?

___

___

Describe the attachment between father and son as it is being acted out in your family.

___

___

Describe the attachment between stepfather and son as it is being acted out in your family.

___

___

5. Read further down page 245. What do the nationwide averages confirm about stepfathers?

_______________________________________________

_______________________________________________

Do you see the importance of a father's role in the life of the children?

_______________________________________________

_______________________________________________

6. What can you do to be a more available parent to your children?

_______________________________________________

_______________________________________________

_______________________________________________

_______________________________________________

7. The story of two couples with two children between them is found on pages 247–251 of *Blended Families*. Despite personal emotions, these people are co-parenting well. When asked how they make divorce work so well, they had one golden rule:

"Their golden rule is to put the ______________ first." (page 251 of *Blended Families*)

How close together do these two couples live? ______________

8. How are the two children, Niko and Jen, adjusting to the new living arrangements?

_______________________________________________

_______________________________________________

_______________________________________________

_______________________________________________

9. Describe how you have laid aside selfish emotions and continued to mature in your ability to work well with your ex, and his or her new partner for the good of your children?

_______________________________________________

_______________________________________________

If you are not yet doing this, will you reconsider now? How could you start?

_______________________________________________

10. Another family's story begins on page 252. What were some of the initial struggles when Susan and Phil blended their families together?

What promise did Susan hang onto?

11. On page 254 Susan's husband, Phil, made a profound statement to her. He said, "We don't have to judge our children. All we have to do is ________ them."

How did that one statement affect Susan's role as a mother?

Would adopting this concept as your own change the way you parent? In what way?

12. At the bottom of page 256 is a verse. Galatians 5:22–23 lists the nine fruit of the Spirit. Explain how each fruit is evident in your life?

Love

Joy

Peace

Patience

Kindness

Goodness

Faithfulness

Gentleness

Self-control

13. Do you think your mate would agree or disagree with you on any of your answers to question 12? Would your children have anything different to say?

Mate

Children

14. Read John 15:1–2. Describe your understanding of God's pruning process.

_______________________________________________

_______________________________________________

_______________________________________________

_______________________________________________

15. Write down a few good things that could happen to your family if each one of you began to grow spiritual fruit?

_______________________________________________

_______________________________________________

_______________________________________________

_______________________________________________

16. Relationships are two-way streets. We cannot cause another person to open up to a relationship with us, even if that person is our child. We can pray and wait for God's timing to come about. Is there a close relationship you would like to see improve? Write down that person's name. ____________________

Compose a prayer asking the Lord to show you how you could open up a new door of communication with this individual. Ask Him to also go before you to soften that person's heart.

_______________________________________________

_______________________________________________

_______________________________________________

_______________________________________________

17. According to Zechariah 4:6–7, what is the only sure way to move a mountain?

_______________________________________________

_______________________________________________

18. Do you recognize God as the true source of your family's progress in blending? Explain your answer.

_______________________________________________

_______________________________________________

_______________________________________________

_______________________________________________

19. What thoughts from the *Epilogue to Blended Families—A Closing Perspective* helped you the most?

______________________________________________

______________________________________________

______________________________________________

______________________________________________

20. Close your eyes and daydream for a moment. Time has passed. Imagine your children are all grown now. In a perfect world, what would the happily-ever-after ending to your blended story look like?

______________________________________________

______________________________________________

______________________________________________

______________________________________________

**A Reflective Moment**

This study has shown us that You, Lord, are in control of the mountains that seem insurmountable to us, and that You have promised us a hope-filled future. Open our eyes to see Your plan for our family's successful blending. Bless us with the wisdom not to judge one another and the willingness to love despite misunderstandings. The truth is, we're all looking to feel loved by those we live with in the same way You continue to love us as the apple of Your eye. There is no greater feeling than to know we are fully loved and fully accepted by our Father in heaven. The next best thing is to experience that kind of joy with our earthly family.

Our prayer as parents is to listen to You so clearly that we will equip today's family and the children of tomorrow with the unwavering knowledge of a God who is faithful to meet their needs.

**Practical Application for your family's future: Turn to page 157 of the workbook and prayerfully complete the *Promise of Commitment* sheet.**

**Leaders: Sign the *Unit Two portion of the Certificates of Completion* found near the back of the book. Go to www.blendedfamilies.net if you would like to print out frameable certificates. Close your class in prayer by reciting together Mother Teresa's *Family Prayer* on page 161.**

# Workbook Enhancement Pages

## Stay Close by, for the Sake of the Kids

7/7/03
By Karen S. Peterson, USA TODAY

When parents divorce, their children do best if both adults continue to live in the same general vicinity, providing both mother and father with proximity to the child, new research shows.

That finding may seem obvious. But it runs contrary to a developing trend in courtrooms, say researchers at Arizona State University. If a custodial parent wants to move, courts are generally approving the relocation, believing that what that parent wants will also be good for the child, the researchers say.

The study indicates that courts should "give greater weight to the child's separate interests" and less weight to a parent's desire to make a move.

"Kids do better with both of their parents to provide some kind of loving environment for them," says study co-author and psychologist Sanford Braver. And that means both parents need to be available to the child, even after a divorce.

The report in the *Journal of Family Psychology*, published by the American Psychological Association, states: "In the great majority of these relocating families (82%), the move separated the child from the father, because either the mother moved away with the child or the father moved away alone."

Young adults from divorced families in which one parent moved did not score as well on 11 out of 14 measures of well-being as those in which neither parent relocated, says researcher William Fabricius. Those measures include general physical health, life satisfaction and personal and emotional adjustment.

They also reported their parents had a worse relationship and were not as available to them for emotional support, compared with those young adults whose parents were not separated by a move.

Fabricius, also a psychologist, is surprised by the study's results. "The fact that we found so many consistently poor outcomes for those whose parents moved is cause for concern."

Findings are similar, he says, whether a parent moved away with the child or whether that parent stayed in place and the other parent moved. It is not the move itself that matters: "It is the separation from a parent" that matters, he says.

Braver is particularly concerned about the findings on the physical health of the young adults studied. "There are implications for the future," he says. "The effects may become exaggerated over time." Prior research indicates divorce can put children at risk for later stress-related illnesses, the report says.

The researchers surveyed 602 college students whose parents had divorced, dividing the students into subgroups that included various moving arrangements — or no move at all.

The researchers emphasize their findings do not indicate a cause-and-effect relationship between a move and a child at risk.

Warren Farrell, San Diego-based author of *Father and Child Reunion*, says the study findings are important. "When one parent is distant, he or she becomes a cardboard figure" in the child's life, he says. "The child ends up destabilized."

# Personality Profile

Created by Fred Littauer

In each of the following rows of four words across, check the one or two words that most often applies to you. Continue through all forty lines. If you are not sure which word "most applies," ask a spouse or a friend, and think of what your answer would have been when you were a child--your natural personality. Use the word definitions on the next page for the most accurate results.

## Strengths

| # | | | | |
|---|---|---|---|---|
| 1 | ☐ Adventurous | ☐ Adaptable | ☐ Animated | ☐ Analytical |
| 2 | ☐ Persistent | ☐ Playful | ☐ Persuasive | ☐ Peaceful |
| 3 | ☐ Submissive | ☐ Self-sacrificing | ☐ Sociable | ☐ Strong-willed |
| 4 | ☐ Considerate | ☐ Controlled | ☐ Competitive | ☐ Convincing |
| 5 | ☐ Refreshing | ☐ Respectful | ☐ Reserved | ☐ Resourceful |
| 6 | ☐ Satisfied | ☐ Sensitive | ☐ Self-reliant | ☐ Spirited |
| 7 | ☐ Planner | ☐ Patient | ☐ Positive | ☐ Promoter |
| 8 | ☐ Sure | ☐ Spontaneous | ☐ Scheduled | ☐ Shy |
| 9 | ☐ Orderly | ☐ Obliging | ☐ Outspoken | ☐ Optimistic |
| 10 | ☐ Friendly | ☐ Faithful | ☐ Funny | ☐ Forceful |
| 11 | ☐ Daring | ☐ Delightful | ☐ Diplomatic | ☐ Detailed |
| 12 | ☐ Cheerful | ☐ Consistent | ☐ Cultured | ☐ Confident |
| 13 | ☐ Idealistic | ☐ Independent | ☐ Inoffensive | ☐ Inspiring |
| 14 | ☐ Demonstrative | ☐ Decisive | ☐ Dry humor | ☐ Deep |
| 15 | ☐ Mediator | ☐ Musical | ☐ Mover | ☐ Mixes easily |
| 16 | ☐ Thoughtful | ☐ Tenacious | ☐ Talker | ☐ Tolerant |
| 17 | ☐ Listener | ☐ Loyal | ☐ Leader | ☐ Lively |
| 18 | ☐ Contented | ☐ Chief | ☐ Chartmaker | ☐ Cute |
| 19 | ☐ Perfectionist | ☐ Pleasant | ☐ Productive | ☐ Popular |
| 20 | ☐ Bouncy | ☐ Bold | ☐ Behaved | ☐ Balanced |

## Weaknesses

| # | | | | |
|---|---|---|---|---|
| 21 | ☐ Blank | ☐ Bashful | ☐ Brassy | ☐ Bossy |
| 22 | ☐ Undisciplined | ☐ Unsympathetic | ☐ Unenthusiastic | ☐ Unforgiving |
| 23 | ☐ Reticent | ☐ Resentful | ☐ Resistant | ☐ Repetitious |
| 24 | ☐ Fussy | ☐ Fearful | ☐ Forgetful | ☐ Frank |
| 25 | ☐ Impatient | ☐ Insecure | ☐ Indecisive | ☐ Interrupts |
| 26 | ☐ Unpopular | ☐ Uninvolved | ☐ Unpredictable | ☐ Unaffectionate |
| 27 | ☐ Headstrong | ☐ Haphazard | ☐ Hard to please | ☐ Hesitant |
| 28 | ☐ Plain | ☐ Pessimistic | ☐ Proud | ☐ Permissive |
| 29 | ☐ Angered easily | ☐ Aimless | ☐ Argumentative | ☐ Alienated |
| 30 | ☐ Naive | ☐ Negative attitude | ☐ Nervy | ☐ Nonchalant |
| 31 | ☐ Worrier | ☐ Withdrawn | ☐ Workaholic | ☐ Wants credit |
| 32 | ☐ Too sensitive | ☐ Tactless | ☐ Timid | ☐ Talkative |
| 33 | ☐ Doubtful | ☐ Disorganized | ☐ Domineering | ☐ Depressed |
| 34 | ☐ Inconsistent | ☐ Introvert | ☐ Intolerant | ☐ Indifferent |
| 35 | ☐ Messy | ☐ Moody | ☐ Mumbles | ☐ Manipulative |
| 36 | ☐ Slow | ☐ Stubborn | ☐ Show-off | ☐ Skeptical |
| 37 | ☐ Loner | ☐ Lord over others | ☐ Lazy | ☐ Loud |
| 38 | ☐ Sluggish | ☐ Suspicious | ☐ Short-tempered | ☐ Scatterbrained |
| 39 | ☐ Revengeful | ☐ Restless | ☐ Reluctant | ☐ Rash |
| 40 | ☐ Compromising | ☐ Critical | ☐ Crafty | ☐ Changeable |

**Now transfer all your selections to the corresponding words on the Personality Scoring Sheet and add up your totals.**

## Personality Profile Word Definations

(Adapted from Personality Patterns by Lana Bateman)

# STRENGTHS

**1**
- **Adventurous.** One who will take on new and daring enterprises with a determination to master them.
- **Adaptable.** Easily fits and is comfortable in any situation.
- **Animated.** Full of life, lively use of hand, arm, and face gestures.
- **Analytical.** Likes to examine the parts for their logical and proper relationships.

**2**
- **Persistent.** Sees one project through to its completion before starting another.
- **Playful.** Full of fun and good humor.
- **Persuasive.** Convinces through logic and fact rather than charm or power.
- **Peaceful.** Seems undisturbed and tranquil and retreats from any form of strife.

**3**
- Submissive. Easily accepts any other's point of view or desire with little need to assert his own opinion.
- Self-sacrificing. Willingly gives up his own personal being for the sake of, or to meet the needs of others.
- Sociable. One who sees being with others as an opportunity to be cute and entertaining rather than as a challenge or business opportunity.
- Strong-willed. Determined to have one's own way.

**4**
- Considerate. Having regard for the needs and feelings of others.
- Controlled. Has emotional feelings but rarely displays them.
- Competitive. Turns every situation, happening, or game into a contest and always plays to win!
- Convincing. Can win you over to anything through the sheer charm of his personality.

**5**
- **Refreshing.** Renews and stimulates or makes others feel good.
- **Respectful.** Treats others with deference, honor, and esteem.
- **Reserved.** Self-restrained in expression of emotion or enthusiasm.
- **Resourceful.** Able to act quickly and effectively in virtually all situations.

**6**
- Satisfied. A person who easily accepts any circumstance or situation.
- Sensitive. Intensively cares about others, and what happens.
- Self-reliant. An independent person who can fully rely on his owncapabilities, judgment, and resources.
- Spirited. Full of life and excitement.

**7**
- Planner. Prefers to work out a detailed arrangement beforehand, for the accomplishment of project or goal, and prefers involvement with the planning stages and the finished product rather than the carrying out of the task.
- Patient. Unmoved by delay, remains calm and tolerant.
- Positive. Knows it will turn out right if he's in charge.
- Promoter. Urges or compels others to go along, join, or invest through the charm of his own personality.

**8**
- Sure. Confident, rarely hesitates or wavers.
- Spontaneous. Prefers all of life to be impulsive, unpremeditated activity, not restricted by plans.
- Scheduled. Makes, and lives, according to a daily plan, dislikes his plan to be interrupted.
- Shy. Quiet, doesn't easily instigate a conversation.

**9**
- Orderly. Having a methodical, systematic arrangement of things.
- Obliging. Accommodating. One who is quick to do it another's way.
- Outspoken. Speaks frankly and without reserve.
- Optimistic. Sunny disposition who convinces self and others that everything will turn out all right.

**10**
- Friendly. A responder rather than an initiator, seldom starts a conversation.
- Faithful. Consistently reliable, steadfast, loyal, and devoted sometimes beyond reason.
- Funny. Sparkling sense of humor that can make virtually any story into an hilarious event.
- Forceful. A commanding personality whom others would hesitate to take a stand against.

**11**
- Daring. Willing to take risks; fearless, bold.
- Delightful. A person who is upbeat and fun to be with.
- Diplomatic. Deals with people tactfully, sensitively, and patiently.
- Detailed. Does everything in proper order with a clear memory of all the things that happen.

**12**
- Cheerful. Consistently in good spirits and promoting happiness in others.
- Consistent. Stays emotionally on an even keel, responding as one might expect.
- Cultured. One whose interests involve both intellectual and artistic pursuits, such as theater, symphony, ballet.
- Confident. Self-assured and certain of own ability and success.

**13**
- Idealistic. Visualizes things in their perfect form, and has a need to measure up to that standard himself.
- Independent. Self-sufficient, self-supporting, self-confident and seems to have little need of help.
- Inoffensive. A person who never says or causes anything unpleasant or objectionable.
- Inspiring. Encourages others to work, join, or be involved, and makes the whole thing fun.

**14**
- Demonstrative. Openly expresses emotion, especially affection, and doesn't hesitate to touch others while speaking to them.
- Decisive. A person with quick, conclusive, judgment-making ability.
- Dry humor. Exhibits "dry wit," usually one-liners which can be sarcastic in nature.
- Deep. Intense and often introspective with a distaste for surface conversation and pursuits.

**15**
- Mediator. Consistently finds him- or herself in the role of reconciling differences in order to avoid conflict.
- Musical. Participates in or has a deep appreciation for music, committed to music as an art form, rather than the fun of Performance.
- Mover. Driven by a need to be productive, is a leader whom others follow, finds it difficult to sit still.
- Mixes easily. Loves a party and can't wait to meet everyone in the room, never meets a stranger.

**16**
- Thoughtful. A considerate person who remembers special occasions and is quick to make a kind gesture.
- Tenacious. Holds on firmly, stubbornly, and won't let go until the goal is accomplished.
- Talker. Constantly talking, generally telling funny stories and entertaining everyone around, feeling the need to fill the silence in order to make others comfortable.
- Tolerant. Easily accepts the thoughts and ways of others without the need to disagree with or change them.

**17**
- Listener. Always seems willing to hear what you have to say.
- Loyal. Faithful to a person, ideal, or job, sometimes beyond reason.
- Leader. A natural born director, who is driven to be in charge, and often finds it difficult to believe that anyone else can do the job as well.
- Lively. Full of life, vigorous, energetic.

**18**
- Contented. Easily satisfied with what he has, rarely envious.
- Chief. Commands leadership and expects people to follow.
- Chartmaker. Organizes life, tasks, and problem solving by making lists, forms or graphs.
- Cute. Precious, adorable, center of attention.

**19**
- Perfectionist. Places high standards on himself, and often on others, desiring that everything be in proper order at all times.
- Pleasant. Easygoing, easy to be around, easy to talk with.
- Productive. Must constantly be working or achieving, often finds it very difficult to rest.
- Popular. Life of the party and therefore much desired as a party guest.

**20**
- Bouncy. A bubbly, lively personality, full of energy.
- Bold. Fearless, daring, forward, unafraid of risk.
- Behaved. Consistently desires to conduct himself within the realm of what he feels is proper.
- Balanced. Stable, middle of the road personality, not subject to sharp highs or lows.

# WEAKNESSES

|  |  |  |
|---|---|---|
| 21 | Blank. | A person who shows little facial expression or emotion. |
| | Bashful. | Shrinks from getting attention, resulting from self-consciousness. |
| | Brassy. | Showy, flashy, comes on strong, too loud. |
| | Bossy. | Commanding, domineering, sometimes overbearing in adult relationships. |
| 22 | Undisciplined. | A person whose lack of order permeates most every area of his life. |
| | Unsympathetic. | Finds it difficult to relate to the problems or hurts of others. |
| | Unenthusiastic. | Tends to not get excited, often feeling it won't work anyway. |
| | Unforgiving. | One who has difficulty forgiving or forgetting a hurt or injustice done to them, apt to hold onto a grudge. |
| 23 | Reticent. | Unwilling or struggles against getting involved, especially when complex. |
| | Resentful. | Often holds ill feelings as a result of real or imagined offenses. |
| | Resistant. | Strives, works against, or hesitates to accept any other way but his own. |
| | Repetitious. | Retells stories and incidents to entertain you without realizing he has already told the story several times before, is constantly needing something to say. |
| 24 | Fussy. | Insistent over petty matters or details, calling for a great attention to trivial details. |
| | Fearful. | Often experiences feelings of deep concern, apprehension or anxiousness. |
| | Forgetful. | Lack of memory which is usually tied to a lack of discipline and not bothering to mentally record things that aren't fun. |
| | Frank. | Straightforward, outspoken, and doesn't mind telling you exactly what he thinks. |
| 25 | Impatient. | A person who finds it difficult to endure irritation or wait for others. |
| | Insecure. | One who is apprehensive or lacks confidence. |
| | Indecisive. | The person who finds it difficult to make any decision at all. (Not the personality that labors long over each decision in order to make the perfect one.) |
| | Interrupts. | A person who is more of a talker than a listener, who starts speaking without even realizing someone else is already speaking. |
| 26 | Unpopular. | A person whose intensity and demand for perfection can push others away. |
| | Uninvolved. | Has no desire to listen or become interested in clubs, groups, activities, or other people's lives. |
| | Unpredictable. | May be ecstatic one moment and down the next, or willing to help but then disappears, or promises to come but forgets to show up. |
| | Unaffectionate. | Finds it difficult to verbally or physically demonstrate tenderness openly. |
| 27 | Headstrong. | Insists on having his own way. |
| | Haphazard. | Has no consistent way of doing things. |
| | Hard to please. | A person whose standards are set so high that it is difficult to ever satisfy them. |
| | Hesitant. | Slow to get moving and hard to get involved. |
| 28 | Plain. | A middle-of-the-road personality without highs or lows and showing little, if any, emotion. |
| | Pessimistic. | While hoping for the best, this person generally sees the down side of a situation first. |
| | Proud. | One with great self-esteem who sees himself as always right and the best person for the job. |
| | Permissive. | Allows others (including children) to do as they please in order to keep from being disliked. |
| 29 | Angered easily. | One who has a childlike flash-in-the-pan temper that expresses itself in tantrum style and is over and forgotten almost instantly. |
| | Aimless. | Not a goal-setter with little desire to be one. |
| | Argumentative. | Incites arguments generally because he is right no matter what the situation may be. |
| | Alienated. | Easily feels estranged from others, often because of insecurity or fear that others don't really enjoy his company. |
| 30 | Naive. | Simple and child-like perspective, lacking sophistication or comprehension of what the deeper levels of life are really about. |
| | Negative attitude. | One whose attitude is seldom positive and is often able to see only the down or dark side of each situation. |
| | Nervy. | Full of confidence, fortitude, and sheer guts, often in a negative sense. |
| | Nonchalant. | Easy-going, unconcerned, indifferent. |
| 31 | Worrier. | Consistently feels uncertain, troubled, or anxious. |
| | Withdrawn. | A person who pulls back to himself and needs a great deal of alone or isolation time. |
| | Workaholic. | An aggressive goal-setter who must be constantly productive and feels very guilty when resting, is not driven by a need for perfection or completion but by a need for accomplishment and reward. |
| | Wants credit. | Thrives on the credit or approval of others. As an entertainer this person feeds on the applause, laughter, and/or acceptance of an audience. |
| 32 | Too sensitive. | Overly introspective and easily offended when misunderstood. |
| | Tactless. | Sometimes expresses himself in a somewhat offensive and inconsiderate way. |
| | Timid. | Shrinks from difficult situations. |
| | Talkative. | An entertaining, compulsive talker who finds it difficult to listen. |
| 33 | Doubtful. | Characterized by uncertainty and lack of confidence that it will ever work out. |
| | Disorganized. | Lack of ability to ever get life in order. |
| | Domineering. | Compulsively takes control of situations and/or people, usually telling others what to do. |
| | Depressed. | A person who feels down much of the time. |
| 34 | Inconsistent. | Erratic, contradictory, with actions and emotions not based on logic. |
| | Introvert. | A person whose thoughts and interest are directed inward, lives within himself. |
| | Intolerant. | Appears unable to withstand or accept another's attitudes, point of view or way of doing things. |
| | Indifferent. | A person to whom most things don't matter one way or the other. |
| 35 | Messy. | Living in a state of disorder, unable to find things. |
| | Moody. | Doesn't get very high emotionally, but easily slips into low lows, often when feeling unappreciated. |
| | Mumbles. | Will talk quietly under the breath when pushed, doesn't bother to speak clearly. |
| | Manipulative. | Influences or manages shrewdly or deviously for his own advantage, will get his way somehow. |
| 36 | Slow. | Doesn't often act or think quickly, too much of a bother. |
| | Stubborn. | Determined to exert his or her own will, not easily persuaded, obstinate. |
| | Show-off. | Needs to be the center of attention, wants to be watched. |
| | Skeptical. | Disbelieving, questioning the motive behind the words. |
| 37 | Loner. | Requires a lot of private time and tends to avoid other people. |
| | Lord over. | Doesn't hesitate to let you know that he is right or is in control. |
| | Lazy. | Evaluates work or activity in terms of how much energy it will take. |
| | Loud. | A person whose laugh or voice can be heard above others in the room. |
| 38 | Sluggish. | Slow to get started, needs push to be motivated. |
| | Suspicious. | Tends to suspect or distrust others or ideas. |
| | Short-tempered. | Has a demanding impatience-based anger and a short fuse. Anger is expressed when others are not moving fast enough or have not completed what they have been asked to do. |
| | Scatterbrained. | Lacks the power of concentration, or attention, flighty. |
| 39 | Revengeful. | Knowingly or otherwise holds a grudge and punishes the offender, often by subtly withholding friendship or affection. |
| | Restless. | Likes constant new activity because it isn't fun to do the same things all the time. |
| | Reluctant. | Unwilling or struggles against getting involved. |
| | Rash. | May act hastily, without thinking things through, generally because of impatience. |
| 40 | Compromising. | Will often relax his position, even when right, in order to avoid conflict. |
| | Critical. | Constantly evaluating and making judgments, frequently thinking or expressing negative reactions. |
| | Crafty. | Shrewd, one who can always find a way to get to the desired end. |
| | Changeable. | A child-like, short attention span that needs a lot of change and variety to keep from getting bored. |

## Personality Scoring Sheet

**Name:** ..................................

Now transfer all your X's to the corresponding words on the Personality Scoring Sheet, and add up your totals. For example, if you checked Animated on the profile, check it on the scoring sheet. (Note: The words are in adifferent order on the profile and the scoring sheet.)

### Strengths

| | **Popular Sanguine** | **Powerful Choleric** | **Perfect Melancholy** | **Peaceful Phlegmatic** |
|---|---|---|---|---|
| 1 | ☐ Animated | ☐ Adventurous | ☐ Analytical | ☐ Adaptable |
| 2 | ☐ Playful | ☐ Persuasive | ☐ Persistent | ☐ Peaceful |
| 3 | ☐ Sociable | ☐ Strong-willed | ☐ Self-sacrificing | ☐ Submissive |
| 4 | ☐ Convincing | ☐ Competitive | ☐ Considerate | ☐ Controlled |
| 5 | ☐ Refreshing | ☐ Resourceful | ☐ Respectful | ☐ Reserved |
| 6 | ☐ Spirited | ☐ Self-reliant | ☐ Sensitive | ☐ Satisfied |
| 7 | ☐ Promoter | ☐ Positive | ☐ Planner | ☐ Patient |
| 8 | ☐ Spontaneous | ☐ Sure | ☐ Scheduled | ☐ Shy |
| 9 | ☐ Optimistic | ☐ Outspoken | ☐ Orderly | ☐ Obliging |
| 10 | ☐ Funny | ☐ Forceful | ☐ Faithful | ☐ Friendly |
| 11 | ☐ Delightful | ☐ Daring | ☐ Detailed | ☐ Diplomatic |
| 12 | ☐ Cheerful | ☐ Confident | ☐ Cultured | ☐ Consistent |
| 13 | ☐ Inspiring | ☐ Independent | ☐ Idealistic | ☐ Inoffensive |
| 14 | ☐ Demonstrative | ☐ Decisive | ☐ Deep | ☐ Dry humor |
| 15 | ☐ Mixes easily | ☐ Mover | ☐ Musial | ☐ Mediator |
| 16 | ☐ Talker | ☐ Tenacious | ☐ Thoughtful | ☐ Tolerant |
| 17 | ☐ Lively | ☐ Leader | ☐ Loyal | ☐ Listener |
| 18 | ☐ Cute | ☐ Chief | ☐ Chartmaker | ☐ Contented |
| 19 | ☐ Popular | ☐ Productive | ☐ Perfectionist | ☐ Pleasant |
| 20 | ☐ Bouncy | ☐ Bold | ☐ Behaved | ☐ Balanced |
| Totals Strengths | ☐ | ☐ | ☐ | ☐ |

### Weaknesses

| | **Popular Sanguine** | **Powerful Choleric** | **Perfect Melancholy** | **Peaceful Phlegmatic** |
|---|---|---|---|---|
| 21 | ☐ Brassy | ☐ Bossy | ☐ Bashful | ☐ Blank |
| 22 | ☐ Undisciplined | ☐ Unsympathetic | ☐ Unforgiving | ☐ Unenthusiastic |
| 23 | ☐ Repetitious | ☐ Resistant | ☐ Resentful | ☐ Reticent |
| 24 | ☐ Forgetful | ☐ Frank | ☐ Fussy | ☐ Fearful |
| 25 | ☐ Interrupts | ☐ Impatient | ☐ Insecure | ☐ Indecisive |
| 26 | ☐ Unpredictable | ☐ Unaffectionate | ☐ Unpopular | ☐ Uninvolved |
| 27 | ☐ Haphazard | ☐ Headstrong | ☐ Hard to please | ☐ Hesitant |
| 28 | ☐ Permissive | ☐ Proud | ☐ Pessimistic | ☐ Plain |
| 29 | ☐ Angered easily | ☐ Argumentative | ☐ Alienated | ☐ Aimless |
| 30 | ☐ Naive | ☐ Nervy | ☐ Negative attitude | ☐ Nonchalant |
| 31 | ☐ Wants credit | ☐ Workaholic | ☐ Withdrawn | ☐ Worrier |
| 32 | ☐ Talkative | ☐ Tactless | ☐ Too sensitive | ☐ Timid |
| 33 | ☐ Disorganized | ☐ Domineering | ☐ Depressed | ☐ Doubtful |
| 34 | ☐ Inconsistent | ☐ Intolerant | ☐ Introvert | ☐ Indifferent |
| 35 | ☐ Messy | ☐ Manipulative | ☐ Moody | ☐ Mumbles |
| 36 | ☐ Show-off | ☐ Stubborn | ☐ Skeptical | ☐ Slow |
| 37 | ☐ Loud | ☐ Lord over others | ☐ Loner | ☐ Lazy |
| 38 | ☐ Scatterbrained | ☐ Short-tempered | ☐ Suspicious | ☐ Sluggish |
| 39 | ☐ Restless | ☐ Rash | ☐ Revengeful | ☐ Reluctant |
| 40 | ☐ Changeable | ☐ Crafty | ☐ Critical | ☐ Compromising |
| Totals Weaknesses | ☐ | ☐ | ☐ | ☐ |
| Combined Totals | ☐ | ☐ | ☐ | ☐ |

# Personality Strengths & Weaknesses

## Popular Sanguine

### STRENGTHS

**Friends**
- Appealing personality
- Talkative, storyteller
- Life of the party
- Good sense of humor
- Memory for color
- Physically holds on to listener
- Emotional and demonstrative
- Enthusiastic and expressive
- Cheerful and bubbling over
- Curious
- Good on stage
- Wide-eyed and innocent
- Lives in the present
- Changeable disposition
- Sincere at heart
- Always a child

**Work**
- Volunteers for jobs
- Thinks up new activities
- Looks great on the surface
- Creative and colorful
- Has energy and enthusiasm
- Starts in a flashy way
- Inspires others to join
- Charms others to work

**Emotions**
- Makes friends easily
- Loves people
- Thrives on compliments
- Seems exciting
- Envied by others
- Doesn't hold grudges
- Apologizes quickly
- Prevents dull moments
- Likes spontaneous activities

### WEAKNESSES

**Friends**
- Compulsive talker
- Exaggerates and elaborates
- Dwells on trivia
- Can't remember names
- Scares others off
- Too happy for some
- Has restless energy
- Egotistical
- Blusters and complains
- Naïve, gets taken in
- Has loud voice and laugh
- Controlled by circumstances
- Gets angry easily
- Seems phony to some
- Never grows up

**Work**
- Would rather talk
- Forgets obligations
- Doesn't follow through
- Confidence fades fast
- Undisciplined
- Priorities out of order
- Decides by feelings
- Easily distracted
- Wastes time talking

**Emotions**
- Hates to be alone
- Needs to be center stage
- Wants to be popular
- Looks for credit
- Dominates conversations
- Interrupts and doesn't listen
- Answers for others
- Fickle and forgetful
- Makes excuses

## Powerful Choleric

### STRENGTHS

**Friends**
- Born Leader
- Dynamic and active
- Compulsive need for change
- Must correct wrongs
- Strong-willed and decisive
- Unemotional
- Not easily discouraged
- Independent and self-sufficient
- Exudes confidence
- Can run anything

**Work**
- Goal-oriented
- Sees the whole picture
- Organizes well
- Seeks practical solutions
- Moves quickly to action
- Delegates work
- Insists on production
- Makes the goal
- Stimulates activity
- Thrives on opposition

**Emotions**
- Has little need for friends
- Will work for group activity
- Will lead and organize
- Is usually right

### WEAKNESSES

**Friends**
- Bossy
- Impatient
- Quick-tempered
- Can't relax
- Too impetuous
- Enjoys controversy & arguments
- Won't give up when losing
- Comes on too strong
- Inflexible
- Is not complimentary
- Dislikes tears and emotions
- Is unsympathetic

**Work**
- Little tolerance for mistakes
- Doesn't analyze details
- Bored by trivia
- May make rash decisions
- May be rude or tactless
- Manipulates people
- Demanding of others
- End justifies the means
- Work may become his god
- Demands loyalty in the ranks

**Emotions**
- Tends to use people
- Dominates others
- Decides for others
- Knows everything
- Can do everything better
- Is too independent
- Possessive of friends and mate
- Can't say, "I'm sorry"
- May be right but unpopular

## Peaceful Phlegmatic

### STRENGTHS

**Friends**
- Low-key personality
- Easygoing and relaxed
- Calm, cool, and collected
- Patient, well-balanced
- Consistent life
- Quiet, but witty
- Sympathetic and kind
- Keeps emotions hidden
- Happily reconciled to life
- All-purpose person

**Work**
- Competent and steady
- Peaceful and agreeable
- Has administrative ability
- Mediates problems
- Avoids conflicts
- Good under pressure
- Finds the easy way

**Emotions**
- Easy to get along with
- Pleasant and enjoyable
- Inoffensive
- Good listener
- Dry sense of humor
- Enjoys watching people
- Has many friends
- Has compassion and concern
- Unenthusiastic

### WEAKNESSES

**Friends**
- Fearful and worried
- Indecisive
- Avoids responsibility
- Quiet will of iron
- Selfish
- Too shy and reticent
- Too compromising
- Self-righteous

**Work**
- Not goal-orientedLacks self-motivation
- Hard to get moving
- Resents being pushed
- Lazy and careless
- Discourages others
- Would rather watch

**Emotions**
- Dampens enthusiasm
- Stays uninvolved
- Is not exciting
- Indifferent to plans
- Judges others
- Sarcastic and teasing
- Resists change

## Perfect Melancholy

### STRENGTHS

**Friends**
- Deep and thoughtful
- Analytical
- Serious and purposeful
- Genius-prone
- Talented and creative
- Artistic or musical
- Philosophical and poetic
- Appreciative of beauty
- Sensitive to others
- Self-sacrificing
- Conscientious
- Idealistic

**Work**
- Schedule-oriented
- Perfectionist, high standards
- Detail-conscious
- Persistent and thorough
- Orderly and organized
- Neat and tidy
- Economical
- Sees the problems
- Finds creative solutions
- Needs to finish what he starts
- Likes charts, graphs, figures, lists

**Emotions**
- Makes friends cautiously
- Content to stay in background
- Avoids causing attention
- Faithful and devoted
- Will listen to complaints
- Can solve other's problems
- Deep concern for other people
- Moved to tears with compassion

### WEAKNESSES

**Friends**
- Remembers the negatives
- Moody and depressed
- Enjoys being hurt
- Has false humility
- Off in another world
- Low self-image
- Has selective hearing
- Self-centered
- Too introspective
- Guilt feelings
- Persecution complex
- Tends to hypochondria

**Work**
- Not people-oriented
- Depressed over imperfections
- Chooses difficult work
- Hesitant to start projects
- Spends too much time planning
- Prefers analysis to work
- Self-deprecating
- Hard to please
- Standards often too high
- Deep need for approval

**Emotions**
- Lives through others
- Insecure socially
- Withdrawn and remote
- Critical of others
- Holds back affection
- Dislikes those in opposition
- Suspicious of people
- Antagonistic and vengeful
- Unforgiving
- Full of contradictions
- Skeptical of compliments

## Enrich Your Relationship

His dominant personality is:

___________

Traits common to the ___________:

1. ______________________
2. ______________________
3. ______________________
4. ______________________
5. ______________________

Her dominant personality is:

___________

Traits common to the ___________:

1. ______________________
2. ______________________
3. ______________________
4. ______________________
5. ______________________

What would you say is a major problem in our relationship as a couple? What would you say is a minor problem for us?

1. Major ______________________
2. Minor ______________________

What solutions could we find to resolve these issues in light of our new understanding of our unique personality traits?

Major ______________________

______________________

Minor ______________________

______________________

I feel our relationship could be enriched if we: (circle those that apply)

___ Set time apart for meaningful conversation
___ Developed better listening skills
___ Did not speak with unkind words or with a critical or sarcastic tone
___ Took a bi-weekly inventory of our priorities as a couple
___ Household and yard chores were shared more equally
___ Made a financial plan
___ Sought outside help for anger or substance abuse issues in our home
___ Found agreement on discipline with the children
___ Begin a family night each week
___ Prayed together
___ ______________________ (write in your thought)
___ ______________________ (write in your thought)

## Effective Communication: Why Body Language Is So Important

Research done at UCLA into communications explained that an audience is influenced by a speaker in three ways:

| | | |
|---|---|---|
| 1. | Spoken Words | 7% |
| 2. | Voice | 38% |
| 3. | Body Language | 55% |

This same research can be brought right down to the communication within our own families. When body gestures account for 55% of our communication, it seems words alone have a very small influence on the listener. It's the tone of our voices and for sure our body language that improves the individual's ability to receive what is being said. Without question, body language speaks the loudest.

The lesson to learn from UCLA's research is that when our body language doesn't match what we say, the body language will most likely be the language that is heard. We are most effective in communicating with others when our words and gestures complement one another.

Some common body languages and their interpretations are:

- A clenched fist indicates strong feelings, like anger.
- Rolling the eyes is a signal of disinterest in the person or boredom with the conversation.
- A smile demonstrates warmth and approval.
- Eye-to-eye contact says *you are important to me. I want to listen.*
- Clapping the hands together, depending on the occasion, could either symbolize appreciation or be a form of rude impatience.
- Crossing arms in front of your chest tells the other person you are closed and protective of yourself, not ready to trust what you'll hear.
- Pointing a finger at someone communicates that you believe you have the right answer and most likely won't consider other opinions.

1. Examine your own body language. List your partner and children one-by-one. Beside their names write down an example of how you believe your body language has been heard by that person.

______________________________________________

______________________________________________

______________________________________________

______________________________________________

2. What could you do differently that would bring your body language and spoken words into harmony with one another?

______________________________________________________________________

______________________________________________________________________

______________________________________________________________________

______________________________________________________________________

## Keep a-Goin'

by Frank L. Stanton (1857–1927)

If you strike a thorn or rose,<br>
  Keep a'goin'!<br>
If it hails or if it snows,<br>
  Keep a-goin'!<br>
'Taint no use to sit an' whine<br>
When the fish ain't on your line;<br>
Bait your hook an' keep a-tryin'—<br>
  Keep a'goin'!<br>
When the weather kills your crop,<br>
  Keep a-goin'!<br>
Though 'tis work to reach the top,<br>
  Keep a-goin'!<br>
S'pose you're out o' ev'ry dime,<br>
Gittin' broke ain't any crime;<br>
Tell the world you're feelin' *prime*—<br>
  Keep a-goin'!

My thoughts about this poem:

________________________________________

________________________________________

________________________________________

________________________________________

Compare this poem to Habakkuk 3:17–19.

________________________________________

________________________________________

________________________________________

________________________________________

## Effective Discipline HYG-5261-96

Melinda J. Hill

Parents struggle with the appropriate ways to deal with the misbehavior of a child. When all of the efforts have produced little results, what is the next step?

Experts suggest that there are three areas that need to be examined before further action is taken.

Ask yourself:

- Why is the child misbehaving?
- How am I handling the misbehavior?
- What specific tools can I find to help me in this situation?

## Why Do Children Misbehave?

Children have their own temperaments, personalities and individual ways of reacting to authority. When rules and limits are placed upon children they may test the rules to the limit to find out how far their independence can go. The expectations set for them by parents may be too strict or too lenient and the children may resort to misbehavior to gain the attention not gained when behavior is good or as normally expected.

Toddlers begin the journey to independence with the establishment of the word "no." Pre-schoolers and school-age children seek limits by testing what authority will allow and what they can get away with. A certain amount of defiance is expected, and healthy, as children establish their own independence.

Each situation will differ in terms of circumstances, personalities and responsibilities.

Parents sometimes have a tendency to compare children with their siblings and peers. Consider each child's growth and development and then ask yourself, "Is this child capable of behaving the way I want?" Have you seen him or her exhibit the manner of behavior you are seeking? Could there be a medical reason that the child can't reach your expectations? Or could there be other reasons that the misbehavior is occurring (a new baby, a move, or a divorce)? Stress in a child might surface as a behavior problem to achieve the attention he or she doesn't receive when acting appropriately.

## How Can I Make My Discipline More Effective?
## Establish Some Home Rules

All family members old enough to participate can be involved in establishing home rules and consequences for violation of the rules. Holding family meetings to establish and regularly review and "update" rules is effective and helps to keep all family members informed and involved. Be sure to share these rules with others providing care to your children (relatives, care givers, etc.) so they will also know what the expectations are and actions they should take when children misbehave.

## Say What You Mean and Mean What You Say

Many times we speak before we think and make demands that we can't follow through with.

"If you cut your toes off with the lawn mower, don't come running to me."

"If you don't clean up the dishes, you won't have dinner for a month."

Don't say something that you can't follow through with. Think about the consequence of certain behaviors before expressing them. Also consider if and how you will be able to administer the consequence. Follow through your command with immediate consequences or rewards for the child's behavior.

## Strive for Consistency

Confronting the behavior, when it occurs, giving the reason it is not acceptable, and following through with the consequence on a consistent basis is the most effective way to change the misbehavior. If we are not consistent in disciplining a child, the child will believe it is all right to act this way sometimes and continue the misbehavior on occasion.

## Use a Firm Voice

Give commands in a firm controlled voice and with an authoritative manner. Don't make it a game for the child to guess if you mean it or not.

## Get the Child's Attention

Make eye contact with the child before a command is issued. Yelling from across the room will not be effective.

## Set Expectations

Don't ask the child to follow a command. Remind the child that you expect him or her to behave in certain ways. Explain what behavior is acceptable and what is not acceptable and what the consequences will be.

## Remain in Authority

Stick to your guns. Don't get talked out of your feelings or your reasons for issuing the command, and don't let the child wear you down.

## One Step at a Time

Even when you have tried everything, having the right attitude will increase the child's self-esteem and offer the limits in a loving way. Chances are that if the behavior worsens, the modification is working. You are tightening the reins and they feel threatened. It will get better with consistent application.

## Where Do I Go for More Help?

If prolonged or acutely severe behavior problems continue to exist after recommended intervention is attempted, then professional help is advised. Determine what services are available in your community through the school system, mental health centers, support groups, etc. Take advantage of services appropriate for your needs.

Caraway, Mitch. (1993) "Dealing With Children With Special Needs." Inservice presented at Northeast District, Ohio State University Extension, Wooster, Ohio.

Parker, Harvey C. (1994) *ADD Hyperactivity Workbook For Parents, Teachers, and Kids.* Florida: Impact Publications, Inc.[14]

# Smarter, Not Harder

## Youth Personality Profile

**Directions:** Each statement describes a personality type. Read each statement carefully; check the one in each row across that most often applies to you. If two apply equally, you may check both.

| 1 | 2 | 3 | 4 |
|---|---|---|---|
| ___ I can make any story or joke very funny. | ___ Sometimes people think I mean it, when I am really joking. | ___ I enjoy a good joke, but not when it hurts someone's feelings. | ___ I have a dry sense of humor and can come up with really funny one-liners. |
| ___ I am excited about the decisions I make. I believe they are good ones. | ___ I like making decisions; I'm usually right. | ___ I want all the facts before I make a decision. | ___ I would rather let others make the decisions. |
| ___ I like being with others, having fun and being the life of the party. | ___ I enjoy the challenge of being in control when I'm in front of a group. | ___ I enjoy being with people, but I also need time alone. | ___ I go with the flow; I'm comfortable anywhere. |
| ___ I love to talk more than I like to listen. | ___ When I talk, people listen and pay attention. | ___ I think before I speak so I do not say the wrong thing. | ___ I listen more than I talk so I don't get into trouble. |
| ___ I make friends easily; people seem to like me. | ___ I like to be in charge when I am with my friends. | ___ I go beyond the surface to discover the real person. | ___ I like to watch people; it gives me a really good picture of what they're like. |
| ___ I get bored if I have to do the same things all the time. I need excitement. | ___ I like taking on new and daring things because of the challenge. | ___ I keep a schedule so that I know what I am doing next. | ___ I like variety. I like knowing a little bit about a lot of things. |
| ___ I can come up with really creative ideas that sound like fun. | ___ I like being productive and getting things done quickly. | ___ I'm always analyzing people, places and things. | ___ Sometimes I compromise to avoid conflict. |
| ___ If I were in a forest, I'd try to find some people; I wouldn't want to be alone. | ___ If I were in a forest, I'd look for the path that would get me out the fastest. | ___ If I were in a forest, I'd examine every detail of a tree, flower, plant or rock. I enjoy nature. | ___ If I were in a forest, I'd see the harmony of how everything fits together; I wouldn't be in a hurry. |

Total your scores here:

_____ _____ _____ _____

Take your totals and place them at the bottom of each appropriate column. Block in your totals for each column. Now you have a basic of what your personality is. The chart on the other side of this page will explain in more detail the characteristics of each personality

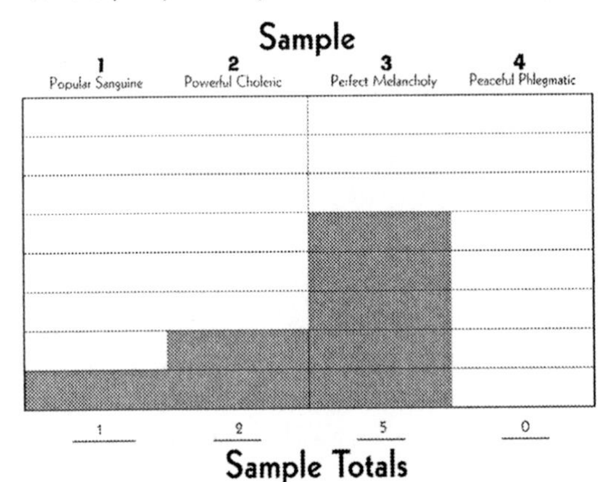


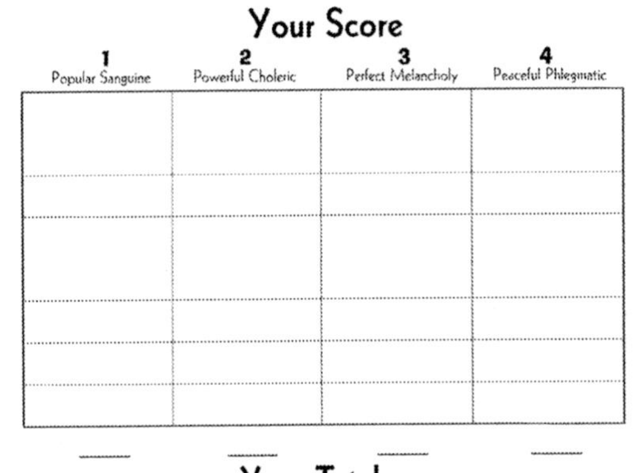


Created by Sharon Marshall Johnson as a part of the nationally-validated SCORE program. SCORE is a co-curricular support program validated by the United States Department of Education for its effectiveness in improving the academic performance of high-risk youth.

Based on the teaching of Florence Littauer & Marita Littauer as found in the best-selling books:
**Personality Plus, Personality Puzzle, Your Personality Tree** and **Getting Along With Almost Anybody**.

# Strengths*

| | Popular Sanguine | Powerful Choleric | Perfect Melancholy | Peaceful Phlegmatic |
|---|---|---|---|---|
| **Emotions** | Appealing personality<br>Talkative, storyteller<br>Life of the party<br>Good sense of humor<br>Memory for color<br>Physically holds on to listener<br>Emotional and demonstrative<br>Enthusiastic and expressive<br>Cheerful and bubbling over<br>Curious<br>Good on stage<br>Wide-eyed and innocent<br>Lives in present<br>Changeable disposition<br>Sincere at heart<br>Always a child | Born leader<br>Dynamic and active<br>Compulsive need for change<br>Must right wrongs<br>Strong-willed and decisive<br>Unemotional<br>Not easily discouraged<br>Independent and self-sufficient<br>Exudes confidence<br>Can run anything | Deep and Thoughtful<br>Analytical<br>Serious and purposeful<br>Genius prone<br>Talented and creative<br>Artistic and musical<br>Philosophical and poetic<br>Appreciative of beauty<br>Sensitive to others<br>Self-sacrificing<br>Conscientious<br>Idealistic | Low-key personality<br>Easy going and relaxed<br>Calm, cool and collected<br>Patient, well-balanced<br>Consistent life<br>Quiet and witty<br>Sympathetic and kind<br>Keeps emotions hidden<br>Happily reconciled to life<br>All-purpose person |
| **Work** | Volunteers for jobs<br>Thinks up new activities<br>Looks great on the surface<br>Creative and colorful<br>Has energy and enthusiasm<br>Starts in a flashy way<br>Inspires others to join<br>Charms others to work | Goal oriented<br>Sees the whole picture<br>Organizes well<br>Seeks practical solutions<br>Moves quickly to action<br>Delegates work<br>Insists on production<br>Makes the goal<br>Stimulates activity<br>Thrives on opposition | Schedule oriented<br>Perfectionist, high standards<br>Detail conscious<br>Persistent and thorough<br>Orderly and organized<br>Neat and tidy<br>Economical<br>Sees the problems<br>Finds creative solutions<br>Needs to finish what he starts<br>Likes charts, graphs, figures, lists | Competent and Steady<br>Peaceful and agreeable<br>Has administrative ability<br>Mediates problems<br>Avoids conflicts<br>Good under pressure<br>Finds the easy way |
| **Friends** | Makes friends easily<br>Loves people<br>Thrives on compliments<br>Seems exciting<br>Envied by others<br>Doesn't hold grudges<br>Apologizes quickly<br>Prevents dull moments<br>Likes spontaneous activities | Has little need for friends<br>Will work for group activity<br>Will lead and organize<br>Is usually right<br>Excels in emergencies | Makes friends cautiously<br>Content to stay in background<br>Avoids causing attention<br>Faithful and devoted<br>Will listen to complaints<br>Can solve other's problems<br>Deep concern for other people<br>Moved to tears with compassion<br>Seeks ideal mate | Easy to get along with<br>Pleasant and enjoyable<br>Inoffensive<br>Good listener<br>Dry sense of humor<br>Enjoys watching people<br>Has many friends<br>Has compassion and concern |

## *Strengths, when carried to extremes, become weaknesses.

For example:

The **Popular Sanguine** strength of being talkative and a good story teller,
when carried to excess, causes the **Popular Sanguine** to exaggerate and sometimes lose sight of truth.

The **Powerful Choleric** strength of being dynamic and active,
when carried to excess, causes the **Powerful Choleric** to become a workaholic and mercilessly drive others to achieve.

The **Perfect Melancholy** strength of being analytical,
when carried to excess, causes the **Perfect Melancholy** to be critical of others and skeptical of compliments.

The **Peaceful Phlegmatic** strength of being easygoing and relaxed,
when carried to excess, causes the **Peaceful Phlegmatic** to avoid responsibility and can sometimes grow into laziness.

## Birth Order HYG-5279-95

Lorie M. Sutter

Birth order is one way to gain an understanding of friends, family members and co-workers. Some researchers believe how you are placed in your family can have an influence on personality traits. Other factors must also be considered. These include genetics and the environment in which you were raised.

There are no magical formulas to help us understand our friends and family. However birth order research may offer "clues" about why people tend to be the way they are. Through your position in the family (birth order) you develop your behavior pattern, way of thinking and emotional response. Your birth order helps determine your expectations, your strategies for dealing with people and your weaknesses.

Understanding birth order may give some insight into a better understanding of yourself and others. Birth order placement may help you know what to expect of others, what to avoid and how to get responses you want. This can be an advantage in parenting, teaching, sales and other occupations.

Psychologists who have studied the impact of birth order on personality have found first-borns tend to be highly motivated to achieve. Of the first twenty-three astronauts sent into outer space, twenty-one were first-borns or only children.

In school, first-borns tend to work harder for grades than do later-borns. They often grow to be more competitive and to have higher educational and career aspirations. Any enumeration of prominent people, eminent scholars, even presidents of the United States contains a high percent of first-borns.

**Characteristics of first borns:**

- Goal setters
- High achievers
- Perfectionist
- Responsible
- Organized
- Rule Keepers
- Determined
- Detail people

Only-children are considered as a specialized type of first-borns. They are generally characterized much the same as firstborns who have siblings.

A good description of middle children is balanced. Middle children are good mediators and have superior cooperation skills. They don't have their parents all to themselves or get their own way. Therefore, they learn to negotiate and compromise. Middle children often make excellent managers and leaders because of these skills.

**Characteristics of the Middle Child:**

- Flexible
- Diplomatic
- Peacemaker
- Generous
- Social
- Competitive

Youngest children in the family are typically outgoing and great at motivating other people. They are also affectionate, uncomplicated and sometimes a little absent minded.

Studies show that babies of the family gravitate toward vocations that are people oriented. Good sales people are often last borns.

**Characteristics of the last born child:**

- Risk takers
- Outgoing
- Idea people
- Creative
- Humor
- Question authority

Birth order isn't a simplistic 1-2-3 system that says all first-borns are equally one way, all second children are another and last-born kids are always just like this or that. These are tendencies and general characteristics that often apply. There are dynamics within families that can change relationships.

Variables can affect each family situation. These variables include spacing (the number of years between children), the sex of the child, physical differences, disabilities, the birth order position of parents, any blending of two or more families due to death or divorce and the relationship between parents.

Whether raising your children or working with adults the key is to remember everyone is an individual. Birth order is another attempt to gain insight into the complex behavior of human beings. [15]

Sources: *The Birth Order Challenge*, by Clifford Isaacson; *The Birth Order Book* by Kevin Lehman (Reprinted with permission of Ohio State University Extension)

# *A Pail of Fresh Berries*

The months of August hold special childhood memories for me. My younger sister and I would race each other up the hill, a pail in one hand, and a pair of clippers in the other. We were heading for the big rambling blackberry vine that sat proud, smack dab in the middle of our pasture. This bush could have won first prize at the county fair. Neither one of us could wait to plop the first sweet blackberry of the season into our mouths. Not even ice cream could have tasted any better than those first berries of summer.

But on that same farm, nothing left a more disgusting memory than a day when I'd unknowingly step into a huge, slippery, smelly cow pie I hadn't seen lying in the grass beneath my feet. I suppose I was looking ahead to the blackberry vine and forgot to watch where I was walking. The fact that the blackberries and the cows shared the same field kind of slipped my mind.

The most unforgettable pies—they were the ones freshly dropped from the cow. They seemed as big as the state of Texas and soft in the center, like old Bessie had been there within the hour. A cow pie like that didn't just mess up the bottom of your shoe, it gushed up the sides as well. Stepping into one of *those* meant you'd have to stop whatever you were planning to do and set about cleaning up the mess. I'd have loved to throw away the shoes, but I only had the one pair. It wasn't an option.

Now that I'm part of a stepfamily, it seems families like mine have a lot in common with blackberries and cow pies. We head out in search of the sweet life but too often find ourselves living in a field of cow pies we didn't know were there. As individuals we don't always stop and think about helping each other, especially those we are not biologically related to, make it safely through the field. Oh, sometimes we do act as sweet as a ripened blackberry with our siblings, parents and partners, but other times we have no more manners toward one another than an unconcerned careless cow.

So what can we do to pay more attention to the blackberries and minimize the cow pies in our families? An attitude of unity is a good beginning. Rather than being self focused, become family focused. Make allowance for everyone to live in the same field. Think first and act second by considering the delicate nature of a ripe berry. Look at one another with the idea that each person is just as fragile as the berry we hold in our hand. Remember to liken words of encouragement and loving correction to the sunshine that ripens the sweetness hidden inside the fruit on its way to maturity. Put too much pressure on a berry and two things happen. You either get a stain that is almost impossible to get out or you reduce your beautiful berries to juice suited only for jelly. Most fruit juice by itself doesn't make edible jelly. A skillful cook adds large amounts of sweetener and patient stirring to the juice before she has a quality product to put on the table. The process of making jelly is similar to the emotional healing a child whose spirit has been crushed from put-downs, name calling, or ridicule, will need to feel worthy again.

Blackberries and cow pies may seem silly, but they can be used to encourage change in our closest relationships. We can set out to have the berry moments outnumber the times that we will encounter the cow pies. Starting today we can choose to nurture an abundant berry harvest. Our plan could include spreading the sunshine of respect to one another, doling out compliments, minimizing criticism, helping with homework, and making time for family fun. We might even decide to get expert help for some of those problematic cow pies that seem to linger.

Any time a family member feels unfairly treated, start looking for a cow pie. Some of these pies might be filled with the unpleasant smell of anger, the stench of jealousy, the slime of secrets kept, the muck of rejection, or the filth of unkind words. Other pies could have us mired in blame, unspoken grief, or selfish competition. Good resources are available for marriage, parenting, grief, anger management, domestic abusive, addictive behaviors, and financial planning.

There is no reason to believe a blended family can't create a plan that activates hope, builds camaraderie, and develops trust between its members. The truth is we can *learn* to live in harmony with one another. It's up to each one of us to do our part to make the experience as delightful as possible. Teamwork is the key. My sister and I didn't go up the hill unprepared. We knew how sharp blackberry thorns could be. So we wore long-sleeved shirts and denim pants, not our shorts and tank tops. We put on lace-up shoes, not rubber thongs. By working together we were able to come back with the least amount of scratches from briars, as little cow muck as possible on our shoes, and a gallon pail full of delicious berries for supper.

## Household Budget Worksheet for Blended Families

**Monthly Income:**

| | |
|---|---|
| Wages | $_____._____ |
| Wages (spouse) | _____._____ |
| Social Security | _____._____ |
| Retirement | _____._____ |
| Alimony | _____._____ |
| Child Support | _____._____ |
| Rentals | _____._____ |
| Investments | _____._____ |
| Interest Income | _____._____ |
| Unemployment | _____._____ |
| Other _______ | _____._____ |
| **Total Income** | $_____._____ |

**Secured Debt:**

| | |
|---|---|
| Home Mortgage | $_____._____ |
| Rent | _____._____ |
| Auto Loans | _____._____ |
| Student Loans | _____._____ |
| Past due Taxes | _____._____ |
| Recreational Vehicles | _____._____ |
| Other Debts | _____._____ |
| **Total Secured Debt** | $ _____._____ |

**Unsecured Debt:**

| | |
|---|---|
| Credit Cards | $_____._____ |
| Personal Loans | _____._____ |
| Other | _____._____ |
| **Total Unsecured** | $_____._____ |

**Monthly Expenses:**

| | |
|---|---|
| Tithe/Contributions | $_____._____ |
| Taxes:Federal | _____._____ |
| State | _____._____ |
| Property | _____._____ |
| Child Support | _____._____ |
| Alimony | _____._____ |
| Child Care | _____._____ |
| School Expenses | _____._____ |
| Clothing | _____._____ |
| Food | _____._____ |
| Medical/Dental | _____._____ |
| Auto: Gas | _____._____ |
| Repair | _____._____ |
| Utilities: Electric | _____._____ |
| Natural Gas | _____._____ |
| Telephone | _____._____ |
| Garbage | _____._____ |
| Water & Sewer | _____._____ |
| Security System | _____._____ |
| Travel/Vacation | _____._____ |
| Insurance: Auto | _____._____ |
| Homeowner's | _____._____ |
| Life | _____._____ |
| Health/Disability | _____._____ |
| Home Maintenance | _____._____ |
| Personal Care | _____._____ |
| Entertainment | _____._____ |
| Subscriptions | _____._____ |
| Dues/Memberships | _____._____ |
| Miscellaneous | _____._____ |
| Other Expenses | _____._____ |
| **Total Monthly Exp** | $_____._____ |

**Budget Summary:**

| | |
|---|---|
| Total Household Income | $_____._____ |
| (-) Monthly Expenses | _____._____ |
| (-) Monthly Secured Debt | _____._____ |
| (-) Monthly Unsecured Debt | _____._____ |
| **Total Disposable Income** | $_____._____ |

## Financial Topics for the Blended Family

Compiled by Charles Marsolini, CPA

1. **The checkbook**: Do we want joint or separate checking and savings accounts? If we keep separate accounts, how will we determine which expenses will be paid from each account?

2. **Sharing financial information**: Have we revealed all our financial assets and liabilities? If not, why?

3. **Child care expenses**: How will child care expenses be handled?

4. **Spending plan**: Have we created a reasonable family budget? Will we develop a yearly financial spending plan? Whose input will be part of the plan? Once established will the plan be flexible or written in stone?

5. **Credit cards**: When should we use credit? How many credit cards should we carry? Will we pay the balance off each month or add to the principal owed?

6. **Financial goals**: How should we set financial goals? Under what circumstances can we revisit and change these goals later?

7. **Life insurance**: Who will be covered by life insurance? Who are the beneficiaries? What provisions will be made for each of the children?

8. **Estate planning**: In the event of your death, do you know how your children will be cared for or how your assets will be dispersed? Should you have a simple will, a living trust, or a testamentary trust? What fits your family's needs the best? Have your wills been updated?

9. **Inheritance**: Is there something of special value from a biological family member that should respectfully be handed down from one generation to another?

10. **Burial plans**: Did you have funeral arrangements made with your prior spouse? If so, how do those plans change now? Have you considered the reactions you may get from your children?

11. **Child support**: How will child support funds be used? Who participates in making decisions about spending the child support we are receiving?

12. **Health insurance**: Who is responsible to provide health insurance for the children? If there is no insurance, who pays for the medical expenses incurred?

13. **Higher education**: Is there a plan to put aside money for your child's college education? Are you planning to take more college courses? Is this an area where some planning still needs to be done?

14. **Children and allowance money**: Do your children get an allowance? If so, is it a fair amount? What purchases do you expect the children to make with their own money? How will you help them make spending, giving, and saving decisions?

15. **Retirement benefits**: Will a former spouse receive a portion of your retirement benefits from a 401K; IRA, or pension? Will you keep a proper attitude in the paying out of these monies?

16. **Assets acquired in this marriage**: Will the assets we acquire during our marriage be held in joint tenancy or kept as separate property?

17. **Premarital agreements**: Did you draw up a prenuptial agreement? What points, if any, in the prenuptial agreement are you willing to renegotiate over time (5 years, 10 years)?

## Successful Money Strategies

Compiled by Charles Marsolini, CPA

1. Discuss your feelings about money. Talk about your past experiences with money. Was this experience positive or negative? Be honest about any problem with the IRS, credit card debt, a paycheck garnishment, or if you've gone bankrupt.

2. Blended families usually choose to manage their finances in one of three ways:

   - The "one purse" approach: all monies are pooled and then distributed according to need.
   - The "two purse" approach: individual partners keep their income and expense accounts separate—each retains control over his or her own finances.
   - The "three purse" approach: a household account is established for joint expenses that both spouses contribute to. At the same time each partner keeps a separate account.

   With joint planning, separate bank accounts for *his*, *hers,* and *our* children can minimize some of the financial differences you will encounter. While this sounds good, it could also create issues that draw lines between family blending.

3. When there is an imbalance of financial resources available for the support of one child, communicate with each child about the family's overall financial situation and the plan that is in use for the payments made by the non-custodial parent (this will depend on the age of the children). By middle school, children are old enough to learn about the family expenses, and are probably hearing from your ex how much support is being sent on their behalf. This is a good time to have your sons and daughters help with spending decisions. Begin by letting them add up the month's bills for food, housing, clothing, transportation, recreation, savings, and other budgeted categories. As a family, work together to decide how the money will be best spent.

4. If possible, allocate a portion of the child support directly to your child for clothing, recreation, and personal expenses. This gives your child an opportunity to learn about money first-hand. Perhaps he can save for his own bicycle; she can buy her own dance dress.

5. Do your best to reach an agreement with the other biological parent about how financial emergencies and unexpected expenses for your child will be met. Be careful not to demand how the other family will spend its money. They also have expenses and you will get more of what you want by being kind.

6. Join a support group for blended families. Remarried families in a similar situation may be able to provide ideas that already work for them.

7. Show appreciation to the former spouse for those little things they've given to the children. If the gifts are extravagant, it might be time to have a diplomatic discussion about whether some of the money spent could be placed in an educational IRA for the child to use later.

8. Continue to talk with the children about the family's finances as they mature. Very few blended families have the resources to maintain the "old" familiar standard of living when there are two households to support. Be careful so that the children in the second family do not resent the children of the first marriage, or vise-versa. Your example both in words and body language are very important. It is vital to avoid using language that leaves children feeling they are to blame for the need of financial support from their parent.

9. Remember to relax your expectations. The truth is there are no perfect solutions. Spend your time thinking about the things you do have power over in your financial situation and worry a whole lot less about those you can't control.

10. Pray for wisdom with your finances. Take a class together. Educate your children with age appropriate children's studies. Crown Financial Ministries offers materials for the entire family. You can contact this resource through *www.crown.org*.

# *Thoughts to Ponder*

Beneath each statement write a few sentences that express your thoughts.

1. Are you feeling downcast? Count your blessings. You have more than you realize. Your list should include, but not be limited to: salvation, health, parents, children, extended family, clothing, shelter, schools, doctors, your job, your church family, your friends, and the city you live in.

   ________________________________________

   ________________________________________

   ________________________________________

   ________________________________________

2. "Let the little children come to me, and do not hinder them, for the kingdom of God belongs to such as these" (Jesus' words- Mark 10:14).

   ________________________________________

   ________________________________________

   ________________________________________

   ________________________________________

3. Think about God's love. Imagine the King of Kings caring so much He even holds the tissue that will wipe the tears from our eyes (Rev 21:4 no more crying).

   ________________________________________

4. By their very nature, therefore, questions about family must also be questions about self. No matter how long we've been on our own or how far we think we've distanced ourselves from the family we grew up with, their rhythms, values, and psychological habits, have, whether we realize it or not, left a deep imprint.[16]

5. We are all diamonds in the rough, created by an almighty loving Father who has a divine purpose for each of us. In their natural state, diamonds are covered in dirt. Some of us have more dirt in our lives than others. But when God removes that dirt, our inner beauty is revealed.[17]

6. Ruthless callous words like gravity fed streams race swiftly from their source as uncontrollable as springtime rain in Rome (reflect on Ephesians 4:31).

7. One of the best ways I know to keep from getting angry when we don't get our way is to have a good sense of humor. Turn the bad times into a little fun.[18]

8. What greater thing is there for two human souls than to feel that they are joined . . . to strengthen each other . . . to be at one with each other in silent unspeakable memories.

—George Elliot[19]

9. Godliness is having a regard for God's glory and God's will in every aspect of our lives, doing everything out of reverence and love for Him.[20]

10. There is a delicious gladness that comes from God. A holy joy. A sacred delight. And it is within your reach. You are one decision away from joy. –Max Lucado[21]

11. Unity within the couple's relationship bridges the emotional gap between the stepparent and stepchildren and positions both adults to lead the family. If a biological parent is not willing to build such a bridge with the stepparent, the stepchildren will receive an unhealthy amount of power in the home.[22]

## Blended Families Workbook: Evaluation Sheet

Thank you for your participation in this study. Please take a few minutes to complete this evaluation and give it to your small group leader.

Name: ______________________________ Date ___________________

1. Our family's blending has *improved/ not improved* (circle one) as a result of this class.

   The greatest improvement has been: ____________________________________________

   ____________________________________________________________________________

   ____________________________________________________________________________

   ____________________________________________________________________________

2. What two subjects talked about in class best met the needs of your family? Why?

   1. __________________________________________________________________________

   2. __________________________________________________________________________

3. Other areas of interest to the blended family that I'd like to see included in this study are:

   ____________________________________________________________________________

   ____________________________________________________________________________

4. Participating in this class has helped *me* to

   ____________________________________________________________________________

   ____________________________________________________________________________

   ____________________________________________________________________________

   ____________________________________________________________________________

5. Would you recommend this class to others? (circle one) *Yes / No*

6. Additional comments:

   ____________________________________________________________________________

   ____________________________________________________________________________

   ____________________________________________________________________________

   ____________________________________________________________________________

*The Lord, the Creator of the universe, wants your blended family to succeed.*
—Jeremiah 29:11

# *Promise of Commitment*

Now that you have completed the *Blended Family Workbook*, there is another step to take. The past eight weeks have prepared you to make a promise of commitment to your family. If you feel ready to make this promise, read and sign this page. The Promise page is a gift of love you will give to your partner sealing a covenant that will be cherished forever. When the time is right, consider sharing your Promise sheets with your family.

*From this day forward, and in front of these witnesses, I, ____________________________, make a public commitment to honor my family in the use of words and actions.*

As God enables me I will:

1. Communicate words of encouragement to my family members
2. Discipline our children with an attitude of disciple making
3. Work together with you to set goals that are attainable and dreams that are possible
4. Forgive as Christ has forgiven me
5. Demonstrate unconditional love with each one of our blended children
6. Respect the satellite family members that are forever a part of our children's lives
7. Exhibit a spirit of cooperation and accountability with our finances
8. Ask for your forgiveness in those times when I might let you down
9. Remember that mistakes are opportunities for lessons to be learned
10. Keep my commitment to nurture our family with prayer and integrity

*Date:* ____________________ *Signed:* ______________________________

*Witnesses:*

___________________________________

___________________________________

# Certificate of Completion

________________________________________

( Recipient )

Successfully completed the

## Blended Families Workbook

*Creating Harmony as You build a New Home Life*

(1 Peter 3:8–9)

Unit One: Given on this ________ day of _____________, 20_____

________________________________________signature of leader

Unit Two: Given on this ________ day of _____________, 20_____

________________________________________signature of leader

# *Family Prayer*

"Lord, make me a channel of Your peace, that where there is hatred, I may bring love; that where there is wrong, I may bring the spirit of forgiveness; that where there is discord, I may bring harmony; that where there is error, I may bring truth; that where there is doubt, I may bring faith; that where there is despair, I may bring hope; that where there are shadows, I may bring light; that where there is sadness, I may bring joy. In Jesus' name, amen.

(A prayer spoken by Mother Teresa each morning with her coworkers)

**Endnotes**

[1] Mother's Treasury, 2000 by Mary Engelbreit Ink., Andrews McMeel Publishing, p. 64–65, "Mother O' Mine," 1980 Mary Rita Schilke Korzan
[2] Mother Teresa, interview by Malcolm Muggeridge, in Something Beautiful for God: Mother Teresa of Calcutta, by Malcolm Muggeridge (New York: Harper & Row, 1971), pp. 98–99
[3] Tonia Triebwasser, The Color of Grace, 2000 Fleming H. Revell, p. 50
[4] Tim Lahaye and Bob Phillips, Anger is a Choice, 1982 Zondervan, p. 156
[5] David Seamands, Putting Away Childish Things (Wheaton, Ill.: Victor, 1982), p. 11
[6] A Little Book of Cherished Poems, Compiled by Kay Anne Carson, Galahad Books, p. 55
[7] Robin Jones Gunn, Mothering By Heart, Multnomah Publishers, 1996, 2002, p. 46
[8] Mary Hunt, Debt-Proof Living, Broadman & Holman, 1999, p. 59
[9] Dave Ramsey, The Total Money Makeover, Thomas Nelson Publishers, 2003, p. 66
[10] Steve Farrar, Dads Walking Faithful, Standing Strong, J. Countryman 2001, pp. 82–83
[11] Lewis B. Smedes, Shame and Grace, Harper San Francisco Zondervan, 1993, p. 97
[12] Dr. Richard Land with John Perry, For Faith and Family, Broadman & Holman, 2002, p. 177
[13] Brennan Manning, The Ragamuffin Gospel, 1990, 2000 Multnomah Publishers, p. 85
[14] All educational programs conducted by Ohio State University Extension are available to clientele on a nondiscriminatory basis without regard to race, color, creed, religion, sexual orientation, national origin, gender, age, disability, or Vietnam-era veteran status. Keith L. Smith, Associate Vice President for Ag. Adm. and Director, OSU Extension.
[15] All educational programs conducted by Ohio State University Extension are available to clientele on a non discriminatory basis without regard to race, color, creed, religion, sexual orientation, national origin, gender, age, disability, or Vietnam-era veteran status. Keith L. Smith, Associate Vice President for Ag. Adm. and Director, OSU Extension.
[16] Susan Piver, The Hard Questions for an Authentic Life, Gotham Books, 2004, p. Chapter 1 p. 1
[17] Barbara J. Hansen, Listen to the Cry of the Child, Wine Press Publishing 2003, p. 82
[18] Charles R. Swindoll, God's Provision, J. Countryman 1997, p. 23
[19] Alice Gray, Steve Stephens, John Van Diest, Lists to Live By for Every Married Couple, 2001 Multnomah Publishers, Inc., p. 170
[20] Jerry Bridges, The Discipline of Grace, 1994 Navpress, p. 51
[21] Max Lucado, The Applause of Heaven, 1990, p. 13
[22] Ron L. Deal, *The Smart Step-Family*, 2002 Bethany House, p. 91

To order additional copies of

# BLENDED FAMILIES
# *Workbook*

Have your credit card ready and call:

1-877-421-READ (7323)

or please visit our web site at
www.pleasantword.com

Also available at:
www.amazon.com
and
www.barnesandnoble.com

To contact the author or invite Maxine Marsolini
as a guest speaker, log on to: www.blendedfamilies.net.

Printed in the United States
47657LVS00002B/339-344

9 781414 101811